NUMBERS

Fun and Facts

NUMBERS
Fun & Facts

by J. NEWTON FRIEND

CHARLES SCRIBNER'S SONS

NEW YORK: 1954

Library of Congress
Catalog Card No. 54-8690

CONTENTS

	PREFACE	vii
	PROLOGUE	ix
I	NUMBER SENSE AND ONE TO ONE CORRE-SPONDENCE	I
II	TALLIES AND COUNTING	7
III	THE ORIGIN OF NUMERALS	16
IV	DIFFERENT KINDS OF NUMBERS	34
V	THE OLD CURIOSITY SHOP	55
VI	THE POWERS THAT BE	77
VII	SQUARES, MAGIC AND OTHERWISE	94
VIII	PALINDROMES	101
IX	NUMBERS, TRADITION AND SUPERSTITION	111
X	NUMERICAL PROBLEMS	158
XI	PROBLEMS WITH DIGITS AND LETTERS	177
XII	PROBLEMS WITH MATCHES AND COINS	183
	APPENDIX	191
	INDEX	201

PREFACE

THIS is not a primer or textbook of arithmetic. Far from it. It has been written with one main object, namely to show how interesting, indeed fascinating, is the study of numbers, their origin, and peculiarities, and of the traditions, legends and superstitions that have, in the course of ages, collected round them.

This little work differs from the numerous other more pretentious volumes of recent years in that it is written in simple popular style so that a reader, possessing no more than an elementary knowledge of arithmetic, should have no difficulty in appreciating and revelling in the curious coincidences, freaks, absurdities and fallacies associated with numbers as described herein. Some of the observations and problems which the reader is invited to study are truly ancient, occasionally dressed in modern garb; many are entirely new. It is hoped that those engaged in teaching elementary mathematics may find herein useful suggestions for brightening the lessons and rendering them more attractive both for themselves and their pupils.

A few references to sources of information have been included to assist the reader who desires to follow up points of special interest. A very brief Bibliography is appended.

PROLOGUE

THE drive for waste paper in Britain has brought many curious books and MSS. to light that have for years lain in cupboards, drawers and attics, undusted and uncared for, save by rats, mice and other vermin.

Recently I had occasion to glance at an untidy heap of books and papers salvaged from the corners and crevices of an old shop—a sort of curiosity shop, where once one could purchase anything from a penny block to an elephant's tusk. It has been kept for close on three-quarters of a century by one Adam, who had died a few weeks previously at the ripe age of 94. He had been a real character, and no mistake, a patriarch, a venerable Bede. His piercing eyes would shine out of the dark recesses of his hinterland as you entered his shop, and you felt like a fly entering a spider's den. But the old man's Victorian courtesy and his evidently kindly nature soon put the customer at his ease. Now the dear old man rests with his fathers; another link with the past has been severed and this in an age when the majority of men do not care a tinker's cuss for refinement and tone.

The shop was now up for sale, its cupboards had been rifled, its attics and cellars cleared; stacks of books and papers awaited the salvage corps. As I glanced superficially at the dusty heaps my eyes caught sight of some straggling sheets, torn and begrimed, that seemed to bear the impress of antiquity. On closer examination it appeared that they belonged to the middle of the 17th century, and were part of a monastic mathematical work. Unfortunately many sheets were missing; of those that remained most were partially mutilated, smudged or otherwise rendered illegible. I rescued all the sheets that I could find, took them home and studied them carefully. It was a heart-breaking task, for a sheet would be missing or entirely illegible just when the MSS. was beginning to be interesting. I did succeed, however, in deciphering, more or less completely, a few mathematical problems, one of which I give here as I found it; others are incorporated in later pages of this book.

THE MONKS' PROBLEM

Two elderly monks sat on a . . . . . bench in the sunshine outside the ancient monastery of Brahmanakraka.

Said one—"Brother, seven is a holy number."

"Thou art right, brother" replied the other, "Praise be to God who . . . . . well"

Said the one—"Brother, behold, here are seven rods that express not the truth—

$$I = VII$$

Wilt thou, by removing one rod only, praise God and restore the truth?"

"I will endeavour so to do my brother, and may . . ."

"I pray thee, dear brother," continued the one, "that thou utter no word until thou hast achieved thine aim."

Seven years elapsed. Silence reigned supreme. Reader, canst thou solve this problem? If after seven years thou too shouldst fail in thy task there is still hope for thee. Thou mayest discover the truth if thou wilt . . .

Praise be to God. The truth shall yet be revealed unto thee.

The MSS. ended in this tantalizing way. For long I puzzled over the solution of this problem. One night it was revealed unto me in a dream. I was astounded at its simplicity. Like most problems it is easy when we know. Will you also try your luck?*

* The solution is given on p. 191.

NUMBERS

Fun and Facts

I

NUMBER SENSE

AND ONE TO ONE CORRESPONDENCE

THE belief that man could at one time converse with animals is very ancient. In the Old Testament Eve is depicted as holding quite a lengthy conversation with the Serpent in the Garden of Eden —a conversation that ended in disaster to mankind.

One morning, many centuries later, Balaam, who lived at Pethor on the banks of the Euphrates, saddled his ass with intent to accompany the princes of Moab (*Numbers*, 22). In the course of the journey the ass three times refused to go forward because it saw the angel of the Lord blocking its path. On the third occasion the ass fell to the ground and when Balaam applied the stick the poor "dumb" animal opened its mouth in expostulation and said "What have I done unto thee that thou hast smitten me these three times?" The faithful creature had not only learned to speak, like Xanthus, the horse of Achilles, which foretold its master's death, but it could count as well.

You will no doubt remember the story of the Walrus and the Carpenter as told by Tweedledee to Alice in Looking Glass Land. The above-mentioned gentry were strolling by the seashore and appear to have been in sentimental mood for we are told that—

[2]

"They wept like anything to see
   Such quantities of sand:
'If this were only cleared away'
   They said, 'it *would* be grand.'

'If seven maids with seven mops
   Swept it for half a year,
Do you suppose,' the walrus said,
   'That they could get it clear?'
'I doubt it,' said the carpenter,
   And shed a bitter tear."

The walrus could count up to seven at least—quite a respectable achievement.

It is, however, only in legend and fiction that animals are credited with ability to count. Mathematics is an exclusively human achievement despite the firm belief of the schoolboy struggling through his multiplication table that arithmetic is distinctly inhuman too.

Number Sense

Although animals cannot count it has long been recognized that many such, including birds, possess a number sense in that they appear able to distinguish between one and two and a larger number. Insects are similarly gifted; thus, for example, the wasp provides a fixed number of spiders for its unborn progeny.

Man also possesses an instinctive number sense quite apart from his more recently acquired skill in counting. With a little practice a man of average intelligence can sense up to 5 or 6 and, under favorable conditions, up to higher numbers still. Probably, however, our early ancestors could in general sense only up to three; beyond three was a crowd.

In order to make quite clear the difference between number sense and counting let us consider figure 1. If we glance momentarily at the first group of dots (i) and immediately turn away we can easily sense the presence of three dots although we had nothing like sufficient time to count them. In scheme (ii) we similarly sense six and, if adept, we realise that there are nine dots in the third group. In the two latter

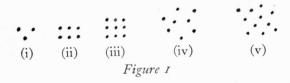

(i)   (ii)   (iii)   (iv)   (v)

Figure 1

cases we are of course aided by symmetrical arrangement. But unless we are particularly astute a momentary glance at the fourth group will not enable us to sense the presence of eight dots with certainty. We might hazard a guess that there are about eight dots, but that is probably as far as we should care to go. The fifth group would leave us completely nonplussed.

Primitive Counting

Man undoubtedly acquired a knowledge of numbers long before he attempted to give names to them just as a deaf and dumb child does before he is taught to count. Man would not at first need special names; he could easily indicate small numbers in conversation by referring to his fingers. This is sometimes termed "unnamed counting."

As the faculty of speech developed the numerals would come in for their share of attention and the art of enumeration or counting would begin. At first man was satisfied with names for the first two or three numbers. The dual system, involving counting up to two, apparently finds an echo in the familiar use of brace commonly used to indicate two pheasants or pistols. Analogous terms are pair, couple, duet, twice, twin and twain.

The ternary or threefold system is illustrated by the modern Hottentot who, when asked how many cattle he possesses, will reply one, two or three as the case may be; if he has more than three he will say "many."

That our ancestors suffered such limitations is indicated linguistically in a variety of ways. Thus, the Latin words *tres* three and *trans* beyond, spring from the same root as do also the French *trois* three and *très* very. Again, the words *once*, *twice*, *thrice* are ancient; there is no "fource," we have to say *four times*. Similarly we refer to x^2 as x "squared" and x^3 as x "cubed"; but we have no special terms for higher powers. x^4 is rendered as x "to the fourth" and so on.

Expressions such as these tell their own story.

One to One Correspondence

It may seem strange that man, having once begun to count, should limit his range to such small numbers as two or three. Many a man must have had more than three wives, children, horses, cattle or sheep. Surely he would know how many he had.

Not a bit of it; moreover he did not need to know. Like the Hottentot he would say he had "many" or something equivalent to that. The fact is, it is easily possible to keep records without being able to count. This will be obvious if we consider a few cases.

In my library I have a few thousand books. Exactly how many there are I do not know; indeed I never have known for I have never taken the trouble to count them. In that I am not unique; have you counted yours? But if a book were missing we should know at once for there would be a vacant place on our shelves. In other words, in a well ordered library there is a place for every book and conversely every book has a place. This is the principle of what is termed *one to one correspondence*.

The train is approaching its destination; the conductor has received a ticket from every passenger. How many passengers are there on the train? The conductor does not know. It suffices for his purpose that for every passenger there is a ticket and that every ticket represents a passenger.

The principle of one to one correspondence offers

a method of keeping stock so simple and effective that it need occasion no surprise to find that it was largely used by our ancestors even in primitive times.

The shepherd would let the sheep out of the fold of a morning and as each left he would place a pebble near the exit. When all the sheep had been released their number would exactly equal that of the pebbles in the pile. At evening the shepherd with the help of his faithful dog would round up the sheep. As he admitted them to the fold one by one so would he cast away one pebble at a time from his pile until the tale was complete. When the last sheep had entered the fold all the pebbles would normally have been cast away. If one remained the shepherd knew the tale was not complete; he would close the fold and set out with his dog to find the stray. If on the other hand a sheep remained outside the fold when the last pebble had been cast aside the shepherd knew that he had one too many.

This method of keeping stock was used in early Roman times. The man who did the checking was known as the "stone" man or "calculator" from the Latin *calculus* a stone. Similarly the Greek word *psephisein* means to reckon while *psephis* denotes a pebble. The connection is obvious.

II

TALLIES AND COUNTING

As TRADE developed it became increasingly necessary both to enlarge the range of counting and to devise more permanent methods of keeping records. In point of time, progress in both these directions overlapped, but it is convenient to deal with them separately in these pages.

TALLIES

The need for devising more permanent records of numbers than piles of stones soon became obvious. If during the temporary absence of the shepherd a wandering animal or malevolent person kicked over the pile of stones, upon his return the shepherd would have no means of checking his flock. This might involve him in serious loss.

The folklore of the Holy Land records that a certain priest of the Orthodox Greek Church was wont to use peas as a means of checking off the periods between successive church festivals. Into one pocket he would put peas equal in number to the days between two successive feasts and every morning he transferred one pea into another pocket. He could thus always tell, on the principle of one to one correspondence, when the next feast was due.

One day the wife of the reverend gentleman, when

tidying his clothes, noticed the peas in his pockets and, thinking he was fond of munching them, out of the kindness of her heart filled all his pockets with peas thus completely upsetting her husband's arithmetic.

To avoid accidents of this kind the pebble method was improved upon by threading beads onto strings or wires. When these were ultimately framed the abacus resulted, with which simple arithmetical calculations could be effected with remarkable speed.

Sometimes cuts or notches were made in wood, ivory, or other relatively hard material for a similar purpose. This procedure was already practiced in Egypt some 1320 B.C. A bas-relief in the temple of Seti I at Abydos represents Thoth, the god of wisdom, recording the duration of the pharaoh's reign by notches on the frond of a palm.

In Europe the sticks or rods carrying the notches came to be known as tallies, from the French *tailler* to cut, from which our word tailor originates. To this custom we owe such expressions as "the accounts tally" and so forth.

Years ago bakers in Scotland, and possibly elsewhere too, used tallies under the name of nicksticks; each family had one such and when a loaf was delivered a nick or notch was made on the stick, and thus a record was kept.

In the Middle Ages tallies were often made of hazel sticks notched by a "tally cutter," as the expert was called. The sticks were then commonly split in two lengthwise, each party to the transaction keeping one-half as evidence. This was a convenient way of preventing fraud, and analogous procedures were practiced widely also in other transactions. Thus, on betrothal, lovers would break a ring in two, each keeping one piece till marriage; they were then put together to confirm the engagement or bargain.

> "A ring of pure gold she from her finger took
> And just in the middle the same then she broke;
> Quoth she: 'As a token of love you this take,
> And this as a pledge I will keep for your sake.'"

Similarly coins were broken in two and the parts brought together again when the bargain or mission had been completed.

Harking back to the tally, at one time when a man deposited money with the Bank of England, the amount was duly registered on a tally stick, which was split lengthwise in two. The tender received one half which was called the stock, or stick, and thus became a stock holder—whence our stock-brokers and stockmarkets.

The incisions themselves made in the wood were known as scores, derived from an old Norse word meaning a cut. Rumor has it that on June 18, 1744 someone at a cricket match in England said for the first time "Let's keep the score" and since then this has become a common expression.

As late as the beginning of the 19th century certain records were still being kept at the Exchequer

Office* in London in the form of wooden tallies; it was not until 1826 that the last tally was issued. By 1834 conversion to a more modern system had been effected and the problem arose as to the disposal of the tallies. These dry fossils of the past were burned in the stoves of the House of Parliament, the dry sticks burned only too readily, the stoves became overheated, and the buildings were set on fire and destroyed, all except Westminster Hall, the Crypt of St. Stephen's Chapel and part of the Cloisters. What Guy Fawkes had been unable to do in 1605 red tape achieved in 1834.

One particularly inconvenient result of the fire was the destruction of the official standard yard and pound, which were then in the custody of the Clerk to the House. There were no official copies.

But out of evil good may come. The loss led to the appointment of a Commission to consider the whole question of standard weights and measures with the result that there is now the Imperial Standard Yard and Pound, the latter Avoirdupois, replacing the earlier Troy. Several exact official copies have been prepared and housed in various places so that if one should be lost the accuracy of the system would not be imperilled.

For many thousand years knotted cords have been used by various peoples as tallies, using that word in its widest sense. In 1872, when taking census in the

* The Office of Exchequer was introduced about 1129, the name originating in the "chessboard" which, with its counters, was used in facilitating calculations before the arabic numerals had reached Britain.

wilder parts of India, knots were made on cords of four colors; black and red for adult males and females respectively, white and yellow for boys and girls. Even today the Peruvian shepherd uses knots in cords to keep check on his flocks, while we often put knots in our handkerchiefs to remind us of a like number of items we do not want to forget.

COUNTING

Simultaneously with the growth of the tally the range of counting was increased. As we have seen, this was at first limited to two or three. Even so, man would be able to count only by pointing to the objects counted, his conception of numbers being entirely concrete. While for example he readily understood that he possessed three children, cows or sheep, as the case might be, the word three by itself, as an abstract number, would convey no meaning to him at all. This helps to explain why we have so many terms to designate different groups of objects and such a variety of units of measurement. Thus, one speaks of a bevy of maidens, a building of rooks, a flight of swallows, a flock of sheep, a gaggle of geese, a herd of deer, a muster of peacocks, a posse of police.

Similarly as regards units of length, we have the foot; the hand, a measure of four inches used mostly in expressing the height of a horse; the span, averaging nine inches; the ell or elbow (Anglo-Saxon *elnbogen*, arm bend) used mainly in measuring cloth, averaging $1\frac{1}{4}$ yards; the barley-corn—the grain from which malt is made; three of these grains were taken as the measure of one inch. Then, too, there is the furlong (of the farmer), the length of a furrow, about one-eighth of a mile; and so on.

No doubt the hand with its five fingers played an important part in enumeration. This is indicated philologically in a number of ways. The Greek word *pente* five, which occurs in such well-known words as pentagon and Pentateuch, is identical with the Sanskrit *pantcha* hand. Then again the word digit, as applied to an integer, is derived from the Latin *digitus* a finger. We can picture early man standing with his spear under his left arm and ticking off small numbers with his fingers, using his right hand as a check off.

To count with the fingers is even today quite common practice. Children invariably do so at an early stage at school, while in the course of conversation or during a lecture adults frequently tick off their points on their fingers as a visual aid to memory.

Our word ten is a contracted form of the Gothic *tai-hund* two hands (pp. 15, 141). It is said that the Sakais of Malaya cannot count beyond ten; as we shall see presently our own system of counting is based on ten.

Group Number 20

When, as business increased, numbers to be recorded were considerable, say 50 or more, as might well be when counting a flock of sheep, a herd of cattle, or when taking a tribal census, time could be saved by making a deeper or longer incision at every twentieth score, just as on our rulers today each inch or centimeter is marked by a longer line than its fractions. This is the origin of the alternative meaning of the word score, namely to indicate twenty. It was in common use as late as the 17th century and is still in use, though more restrictedly, today.

In the words of the Psalmist (*Psalm* 90: 10) as given in the Authorized Version of the Scriptures dated 1611—

"The days of our years are three-score years and ten; and if by reason of strength they be four-score years, yet is their strength labour and sorrow."

Fortunately today many of us can discard the final gloomy statement.

Students of English history may recall the memory of sturdy William Walworth, one of the very few Lord Mayors of London famous for his martial deeds. It was he who, in 1381, struck down the rebel Wat Tyler, when he threatened the young King Richard II in Smithfield. For this Walworth was knighted. Two years later he died and was buried at St. Michael's in Crooked Lane. A monument, unhappily destroyed in the Great Fire of London, 1666, bore a lengthy inscription describing the event and ending with the words—

"He left this lyff the yere of our Lord
Thirteen hundred four score and three odd"

The French indicate 80 by quatre-vingts, that is, four twenties, while 70 is soixante-dix or sixty (i.e. three score) and ten.

The score in these cases is known as the *radix*,

basis of counting or *group number;* an arithmetical system based on the score is termed a vicenary or vigesimal scale, from the Latin *vigesimus* twentieth. As the fingers and toes of humans normally add up to 20, this may be regarded as a natural system and reminds us of the time when our ancestors walked barefoot.

The expression "a score of times," once in common use to denote a large but indefinite number, illustrates the tendency to use group numbers in a popular sense usually to indicate a considerable but indefinite number. We shall find many other examples as we proceed.

Group Number 5

The fingers on the normal hand add up to five and some primitive races used five as their group number. Such a system is termed quinary from the Latin *quinque* five, and may well have been the first to be used extensively.

The Mayas of Yucatan in Central America somewhere about 500 A.D. had adopted a combination of the quinary and vigesimal systems. A dot represented unity; two, three and four dots indicated like numbers but five was denoted by a bar. Six, represented by a bar accompanied by a dot, was thus five plus one, and so on. Twenty was indicated by a separate sign, and again so on.

| 1 | 2 | 3 | 4 | 5 | 6 | 11 |

Figure 2. MAYAN NUMERATION

Group Number 12

A couple of centuries ago the ancient duodecimal system, from the Latin *duodecimus*, twelfth, based on twelve or the dozen as group number, was very popular. Twelve is the least number with four divisors other than unity and itself, namely 2, 3, 4 and 6. Five, on the other hand, has no divisors and ten has only two, namely 2 and 5. This made 12 a particularly easy number to handle and the one-time popularity of the duodecimal system is today evidenced by the number of inches in a foot, lines in an inch, pence in a shilling, units in a dozen, months in a year and ounces in the old Troy pound.

Group Number 10

At the present time the denary or decimal system is universal among civilized peoples. The word ten appears to have been derived from a compound word meaning two hands. In Gothic—an ancient Teutonic language—the numeral was known as *taihun* or *taihund*, that is, two hands. In accordance with the natural laws governing the variation of consonants in the Indo-Germanic language, taihun appears as *decem* in Latin, from which our word decimal is derived. In the English word ten the gutteral Gothic *h* has disappeared.

The names of integers above ten are based on ten. Thus eleven = *ein lif* or one (German *ein*) left (over); twelve is similarly two left over, while thirteen (three + ten), fourteen, etc. speak for themselves. Twenty is twain tig or two tens, thirty is three tens, and so on. Dozen is the Latin *duodecim* ten plus two.

III

THE ORIGIN
OF NUMERALS

THE use of two kinds of strokes or nicks to indicate digits and scores respectively is inconveniently cumbersome when large numbers have to be dealt with. One hundred and nineteen, for example, would be marked down as five score and nineteen digits. Thus | | | | | ııııııııııııııııııı . This is too clumsy to be acceptable; it takes a relatively long time both to write and to read. A more efficient system could obviously be evolved if we were to invent new signs for small groups of digits and for certain larger numbers as well.

This the Romans did by introducing separate symbols for 5 and 10, namely V and X respectively, and also for certain multiples of 10, namely L for 50 and C for 100. These sufficed for all ordinary purposes; to these M for 1,000 and D for 500 were subsequently added. These were a wonderful improvement. To simplify matters still further an elementary conception of numerical position or place-value was invented; a small number was regarded as either subtracted from or added to a larger, according to whether it preceded or succeeded it. Thus, while IX represented nine, XI was eleven; and so on. One hundred and nineteen, instead of involving five long and nineteen short strokes, could be represented as CXIX, which was both simple to write and easy to read.

Roman numeral letters alternate between multiples of five and two. Thus:

$$V = 5 = I \times 5$$
$$X = 10 = V \times 2$$
$$L = 50 = X \times 5$$
$$C = 100 = L \times 2$$
$$D = 500 = C \times 5$$
$$M = 1000 = D \times 2$$

This would appear to be an echo of the five fingers and two hands used in early numeration. Also be it noted, the sum of the numeral letters in common use by the early Romans, namely I, V, X, L, C and D is 666, the cabalists' number for the Beast in the Book of the Revelation (p. 152).

Roman Multiplication

For mere enumeration the Roman system was both simple and clear, but for the more serious operations of multiplication and division it was entirely unsuited. No wonder the Romans never became arithmeticians.

The essence of multiplication is repeated addition. Suppose for example we multiply 366 by three; this is equivalent to adding three 366's together, and we can do that as follows:

$$
\begin{array}{r}
366 \\
366 \\
\underline{366} \\
1098
\end{array}
$$

To us this may seem childishly simple. Nevertheless one of the Nobel Prize Winners in 1952 is reputed to have confessed that at school he could never do arithmetic. "When I wanted to find out what eight times nine was," he said, "I had to put down eight rows of nine dots and add them up."

A more convenient method, however, has been invented, the method we were taught when we went to school. Thus—

$$\begin{array}{r} 366 \\ 3 \\ \hline 1098 \end{array}$$

This is known as simple multiplication. But the Roman schoolboy could not use this method, his symbols were not sufficiently adaptable. He was perforce compelled to use cumbersome repeated addition. Let us see how this works out. 366 becomes CCCLXVI and if we add three of these together we obtain—

CCC			L	X	V	I
CCC			L	X	V	I
CCC			L	X	V	I
CCC	CCC	CCC	LLL	XXX	VVV	III

To be serviceable this must be simplified; let us do it in stages—

Since V + V = X, the expression becomes

CCC, CCC, CCC, LLL XXXX V III

But XXXX = XL, whence

CCC, CCC, CCC LLLXL V III

and LXL = XC, whence

CCC, CCC, CCC, LLXC V III

also LL = C, whence

C, CCC, CCC, CCC XC V III

and finally

MXCVIII

= 1098

The same result is ultimately obtained, of course, but how laboriously. Imagine the complexity of merely squaring 366. Evidently before mathematics could be further developed a more convenient system of numeration had to be invented.

THE IDEAL NUMERICAL SYSTEM

In order to yield a maximum flexibility, a numerical system must conform to four requirements.

1. *Simple Symbols*

There must be a characteristic, easily written and easily recognized sign for each integer up to, but not necessarily including, the group number. Thus in our denary system we have separate symbols for the digits 1 to 9.

2. *Unit Differences*

There should be unit difference in value between any two successive digits, giving a uniform stepwise ascent from unity up to the group figure. In the Roman system the gaps between I, V, X, etc. are unequal. In our system

$$1 = 2 - 1 = 3 - 2 = 4 - 3 \text{ and so on.}$$

3. *The Concept of Position or Place Value*

As we have seen (p. 16) the Romans had an elementary conception of place value, but it was insufficient to enable multiplication or division to be accomplished with ease.

Modern procedure consists in assigning to each position occupied by a digit a definite place value entirely independent of the magnitude of adjoining digits. Thus in 42, the 4 has a value ten times its normal value; it has precisely the same value in 242 and in 648 simply because it occupies the second position. It is the number, not the magnitude, of the digits to the right of the 4 which decides its place value; the digits to the left are entirely without influence.

4. *The Cipher*

If we subtract I from VI the result is V. Similarly subtraction of 1 from 51 would appear to leave 5. This is manifestly untrue; some sign is necessary to show that the 5 still occupies the second position.

It was for this reason that the cipher was invented—a sign without magnitude. Thus $51 - 1 = 50$

The sole purpose of the 0 is to show that the 5 occupies the second place.

THE HINDU-ARABIC NUMERALS

It seems fairly certain that the Arabs obtained their numerals from the Hindus of India, and these in their turn may have derived them from China. The numerals reached Baghdad, the great center of Arabic culture, in the middle of the 8th century and were introduced into Central Europe several centuries later, probably around 1100. Simple rules for arithmetical calculations came to be known as Algarism or Algarithm, now usually spelt with an o, thus Algorithm. This has nothing whatever to do with the very similar word logarithm derived from the Greek *logos* reason and *arithmos* number. Algorithm owes its origin to the famous Arabian mathematician Abu Jáfar Mohammed Ben Musa, more usually known as Al Khowârizmî, or Al Khwarâzmi, that is, native of Khwarzm. In A.D. 830 he wrote a book explaining the use of the numerals. This work holds an important place in the history of mathematics, a Latin translation of which, under the title *Liber Algorismi de Numero Indorum*, by Adelard of Bath c.1120, caused the numerals to be known in Europe.

Al Khwarâzmi would no doubt have felt honored had he known that, many centuries later, he was to be dubbed a King. In a manuscript in the possession of the British Museum dating from c.1300, dealing with the "Crafte of Nombrynge," the author quaintly explains the origin of the word algorym as follows—

"This boke is called the boke of algorym or Augrym after lewder use. And this boke tretys the Craft of Nombryng, the quych crafte is also called Algorym. Ther was a kyng (sic) of Inde the quich heyth Algor, & he made this craft. And aft his name he called hit algory."

The numerical signs as used by us today developed during trade relations with many countries and were no doubt greatly influenced by these, for we know that they passed through various changes before settling down, by the 15th or 16th centuries, to substantially the same forms as are now in common use.

Figure 3. THE NUMERALS AS WRITTEN IN
THE CODEX VIGILANUS, A.D. 976

The earliest European manuscript extant containing the numerals is the Codex Vigilanus written in A.D. 976 in a monastery at Albelda near Logroño in Spain* (Fig. 3).

* Hill, "Development of Arabic Numerals in Europe" (O.U.P., 1915) p. 28.

For several centuries there existed considerable prejudice against the use of the Hindu-Arabic numerals in preference to the Roman. This is understandable, because the latter were known to everyone and they answered all ordinary requirements very satisfactorily. But by the 15th century the new system had become fairly widely accepted, as was inevitable with the growth of mathematics. The invention of printing helped enormously in this as in other studies both by spreading the information and standardizing the forms assigned to the symbols.

Origin of the Hindu-Arabic Numerals

ONE

1 is undoubtedly the finger.

TWO AND THREE

2 and 3 perhaps owe their origin to "counting stalks" or "computing rods" as they are variously termed. These were short rods or bamboo sticks laid on a table or other flat surface for convenience in calculation. In China they were already in use around 540 B.C. and were usually laid horizontally thus ═ and ☰ . Farmers and others have frequently used match sticks in a similar way to help them in their calculations.

On the well-known principle that to raise the stylo or pen increases the effort of writing and slows the process up, it would seem inevitable that as the symbols came to be written, ═ would tend to become

Z and ≡ change to Ƶ , ultimately shortening into ⸮
as the lowest line was seen to be unnecessary.

FOUR

Now what about 4? We do not really know its
origin. A plausible suggestion is that four, being the
first perfect square, was represented by four computing rods as □ , gradually reduced to ⁂ and
ultimately 4. In 1858 Dr. J. Wilson believed he had
succeeded in tracing the square four through different East Indian script characters in much this
way.

In a manuscript of the second half of the 13th
century a four appears written like the modern 4.
Various forms of a looped four occur in early manuscripts (fig. 3). Both 4 and the looped symbol ⅄
occur on many Swiss coins of the 15th century.
A looped four occurs also on the Viennese statuette
of Marcus Aurelius in the date 1470 (p. 30).

Against the west wall of the north transept in the
beautiful old church of St. Peter at Wolverhampton,
England, stands an old decayed tombstone brought
in from the churchyard several years ago in order to
arrest erosion. In places the description is indecipherable and the difficulty of reading the remainder
is enhanced both by the unusual spelling and the
lack of regular spacing between the words. After
spending a considerable time studying the stone, I
believe the following is a correct rendering of the
legible portion—

HEAR LIETH
THE BOODE OF
WALLTAR SOUT
HALL AND HE IS
LEADHER TO TAK
HIS RESTAND
IHOPIS SOUL IN
HEAVEN IS BLAST
(?) AG 48 X 1444

which in modern English would read

Here lieth the body of Walltar Southall
and he is laid here to take his rest. I
hope his soul in Heaven is blest
(?) aged 48 . . . 1444

The date might equally be 1441 as the end digit is badly eroded; but the two middle fours are very clear.

This is the earliest English tombstone that I know to bear a four of this shape. As has already been mentioned (p. 17) Roman numerals were largely used in the Middle Ages on tombstones and the practice has not even yet died out.

FIVE AND SIX

We do not know the origins of the symbols 5 and 6. It has been plausibly suggested that they may have been derived from computing rods arranged as 5 ⬓ respectively. One would like to think that this was true, but evidence is lacking, appearances are apt to be deceptive and plausible explanations to be untrue.

The five of the Codex Vigilanus (p. 26) is reminiscent of the Roman V often written as U. In later manuscripts it appears in a variety of forms, but from the 16th century onwards a symbol similar to our 5 has been commonly used.

The six shown in fig. 5 appears as ᑫ in an 11th century manuscript.

SEVEN

Our symbol would appear to be derived from the Arabic *sebá*, V, seven. When changing from one language to another symbols frequently rotate through 90° to 180°. The seven in the Codex Vigilanus (fig. 5) is similar to that in common use today. In many early manuscripts, however, it appears like the Arabic sebá V and in others as its inversion Λ. The upright 7 occurs again 1470 on the tomb of the first Earl of Huntly in Elgin Cathedral, Scotland, and this is the common form in manuscripts of the 16th century onwards. The same year, 1470, is inscribed as 1870 on the sole of the right sandal of a statuette of Marcus Aurelius on horseback in the Museum at Vienna. The seven is "drunk" but the right slope is longer than the left. The looped four has already been mentioned (p. 28).

EIGHT

If we accept the square theory for the four, it is easy to regard eight as two fours. In the Codex Vigilanus and in many later manuscripts the eight is similar to that in common use today.

NINE

This is thought to have been derived from the Greek *theta* θ. The transition is simple. In Attic Greek, that is Greek as spoken and written in Athens, θ was used to denote nine. In the Codex Vigilanus the nine resembles the modern symbol.

CIPHER, ZERO OR NOUGHT

The earliest known occurrence of the cipher in India is in an inscription at Gwalior dating back to A.D. 876; but it was certainly known long before then. It appears to have been invented by a Hindu genius somewhere around 100 B.C. Like many a flower he was born to blush unseen, for his name is lost in antiquity—a pity when so many less deserving names adorn or stain our annals. The cipher is supposed to represent an empty space, possibly a field or a blank column in an abacus. It was aptly described by the mathematical Bishop Berkeley (1685–1753) as "the ghost of a departed quantity."

The Hindus used their already existing word *sunya*, which means an empty space or a void, to denote 0. The corresponding Arabic word is *sife* from which we obtain our words zero and cipher. The real mathematical import of 0 was for long not fully understood, and the word cipher came to be used to indicate something secret or hidden. Thus to write in cipher was to employ a secret script, to read which it was necessary to de-cipher. The word "indecipherable" is used in this sense on p. 28.

Even after the acceptance of the Hindu-Arabic numerals, mathematicians were slow to take full advantage of them. As late as the 13th century multiplication was effected in a cumbersome manner by repeated doubling and, if necessary, subsequent addition or subtraction of the various products. This is known as the duplation method. Thus, to multiply 46 by 15, the following steps were involved—

$$46 \times 1 = 46 \qquad\quad = 46$$
$$46 \times 2 = 46 + 46 = 92$$
$$46 \times 4 = 92 + 92 = 184$$
$$46 \times 8 = 184 + 184 = 368$$

$$\text{whence } 46 \times 15 \qquad = 690$$

This certainly avoided the memorizing of multiplication tables other than the twice times, which would greatly please the modern schoolboy, but it was absurdly protracted. In 1384 one writer clumsily wrote the date as 1000.300.80.4 replete with full stops.

For many centuries after the principles of multiplication had been laid down, the illiterate continued to use the old Roman system of repeated addition. Charles Dickens describes this beautifully in "Our Mutual Friend." The elderly Mr. Boffin, whose education had been sadly neglected in his youth, arranged with Silas Wegg, a wooden-legged street-vendor, to have each evening, Sundays excepted, lessons in the art of reading. The said Wegg was to receive the munificent sum of twopence halfpenny per hour for his services, each lesson to be of two hours' duration at the said Mr. Boffin's residence. And this is how the worthy Mr. Boffin calculated Wegg's weekly emolument—

"'Twopence halfpenny an hour,' said Boffin, taking a piece of chalk from his pocket and getting off the stool to work the sum on the top of it in his own way; '-two long'uns and a short'un—twopence halfpenny; two short'uns is a long'un, and two two long'uns is four long'uns—making five long'uns; six nights a week at five long'uns a night,' scoring them all down separately, 'and you mount up to thirty long'uns. A round'un! Half-a-crown!'

"Pointing to this result as a large and satisfactory one, Mr. Boffin smeared it out with his moistened glove, and sat down on the remains."

IV

DIFFERENT KINDS OF NUMBERS

IN ONE of his poems the inimitable Tom Hood de-scribed British legal luminaries as

"Big Judges, little Judges and Judges of Assize."

Just as there are different kinds of judges, great and small, learned and mediocre, kind and harsh, so there are many different kinds of numbers. Let us now consider a few of these.

Odds and Evens

The distinction between odd and even numbers is one of the most ancient of arithmetical conceptions, as indeed we might expect. Already in the Chinese Classics of 1150 B.C. numbers were divided into two groups, male and female or odd and even. We shall have occasion to refer to this again in a later chapter (p. 112).

Digits

As we have already seen (p. 12), the hands played an important part in primitive counting. The normal man has ten fingers all told, including the thumbs, and it appears probable that the term digit originally included the numbers 1 to 10 inclusive.

But language changes with the habits of the people. By the middle of the 16th century, the conception of 10 as a digit appears to have been dropped. Robert Recorde, writing c.1542, stated—

"A digit is any number under ten."

As Robert was the most influential mathematician of his day, we may take it that he voiced the "official opinion." At this time, too, unity or one was not regarded as a number but as a builder of numbers (p. 114), so the digits comprised the numbers 2 to 9. Today practice varies, the term digit referring to the nine figures 1 to 9 or the ten figures 0 to 9 at will.

Integers

As their name implies integers—Latin *in* not, *tangere* to touch—are whole or intact numbers; they may comprise one or more digits, but they contain no fractions or parts broken off. Thus 3, 36, 365, etc. are integers.

Cardinals and Ordinals

Cardinal numbers denote quantity only without regard to priority or precedence. Thus we speak of three men in a boat, the seven wonders of the world, the twelve signs of the zodiac, and so on. For arithmetical purposes quantity was regarded as all-important, arithmetic hinged on it, hence the word cardinal from the Latin *cardo* a hinge. For the same reason certain ecclesiastics are known as cardinals; they are all-important, the organization of the church depending upon their activities.

Ordinal numbers, on the other hand, denote the

order of priority. Thus, according to Holy Writ, Adam was the first man and Eve the first woman; the statement gives no indication whatever of the number of men and women who have existed since the appearance of Adam and Eve.

Amicable Numbers

Two numbers are said to be amicable when the sum of the divisors of the one gives the other, and the sum of the divisors of the other gives the one.

This is not really as complex as it sounds. Two such numbers are 220 and 284. Thus

Number	Divisors	Sum of Divisors
220	1, 2, 4, 5, 10, 11	284
	20, 22, 44, 55, 110	
284	1, 2, 4, 71, 142	220

For a long time these were the only two known; in 1636 Fermat discovered a second pair, namely 17,296 and 18,416. Since then other pairs have been found but all are on the high side.

Concrete and Abstract Numbers

The earliest concept of numbers was inevitably associated with objects. Such numbers are termed concrete. It must have taken many years for man to realize that numbers may also be abstract, that is, entirely divorced from material objects. Thus when we say that four and three make 7, this remains true whether we have men, sheep, houses, years, or any other concepts in mind. Such numbers are abstract.

Multiplication involves a series of additions or repetitions and at least one of the terms involved must be abstract. Thus if we have 3 books and wish for 9, we cannot say

$$3 \text{ books} \times 3 \text{ books} = 9$$

Such an expression means nothing. What we actually do is this: we select 3 books 3 times or

$$3 \text{ books} \times 3 \text{ times} = 9 \text{ books}$$
$$\downarrow \qquad\qquad \downarrow \qquad\qquad \downarrow$$
$$\text{concrete} \qquad \text{abstract} \qquad \text{concrete}$$

Only processes of addition and subtraction can be performed with concrete numbers alone.

A simple problem in English currency will illustrate this still further. What is the result of multiplying six shillings and eightpence by three shillings and fourpence?

Let us see what will happen if we attempt to apply the ordinary rules of arithmetic. The two amounts are respectively $\frac{1}{3}$ and $\frac{1}{6}$ of one pound sterling. If therefore we multiply them together we have—

$$\frac{1}{3} \quad \times \quad \frac{1}{6} \quad = \frac{1}{18} \text{ of } \pounds 1 = 13\frac{1}{3} \text{ pence}$$
$$\downarrow \qquad\quad \downarrow \qquad\quad \downarrow \qquad\qquad\qquad \downarrow$$
$$\text{concrete} \quad \text{concrete} \quad \text{concrete} \qquad\quad \text{concrete}$$

But the calculation may be carried out in another way. Six shillings and eightpence are equivalent to 80 pence and three shillings and fourpence to 40. Hence on multiplication

$$80 \quad \times \quad 40 \quad = 3200 \text{ pence}$$
$$\downarrow \qquad\quad \downarrow \qquad\qquad \downarrow$$
$$\text{concrete} \quad \text{concrete} \quad \text{concrete}$$

This is a very different result and shows the absurdity of attempting to multiply two concrete numbers together.

Concrete numbers may, however, be added or subtracted if desired. Thus if added together as they stand in the original problem the two numbers yield exactly 10 shillings; if, on the other hand, they are reduced to pence and then added they yield 120 pence, which again is 10 shillings.

When we enter a shop to buy, say, three buns at 5¢ each we put down 15¢ on the counter, which the shop-keeper accepts in exchange. At first sight it might appear that we are multiplying two concrete numbers together to arrive at the price; thus—

$$3 \text{ buns} \times 5¢ = 15¢$$

But this is not the case. What has actually occurred is this—

Each bun costs 5¢.

For each bun we purchase we put down 5¢.

If therefore we purchase 3 buns we must put 5¢ on the counter 3 times on the principle of one to one correspondence. Whence—

$$5¢ \quad \times \quad 3 \text{ times} \quad = \quad 15¢$$
$$\downarrow \qquad\qquad \downarrow \qquad\qquad \downarrow$$
$$\text{concrete} \quad \text{abstract} \quad \text{concrete}$$

Real and Imaginary Numbers

The numbers we have dealt with thus far have been real numbers. But just as events may be real, as recorded in history, or purely imaginary as related in fiction, so numbers may be real or imaginary.

For example, no known number when squared can give us -1; hence the square root of -1, viz. $\sqrt{-1}$, is an imaginary quantity; it is often written as i and termed the "complex unity"; it is a most useful conception in mathematics.

Other imaginary numbers are $\sqrt{-2}$, $\sqrt{-3}$ and so on. All of these behave like any other number when subjected to ordinary mathematical processes. Thus, for example—

$$\sqrt{-1} + \sqrt{-1} = 2\sqrt{-1}$$
$$\sqrt{-1} \times \sqrt{-1} = (\sqrt{-1})^2 = -1$$
$$\sqrt{-1} \times \sqrt{+1} = \sqrt{-1} \times 1$$
$$= \sqrt{-1}$$
$$\sqrt{-1} \times \sqrt{-1} \times \sqrt{-1} = (\sqrt{-1})^3$$
$$= (\sqrt{-1})^2 \sqrt{-1} = -\sqrt{-1}$$
$$\sqrt{-1} \times \sqrt{-1} \times \sqrt{-1} \times \sqrt{-1} = (\sqrt{-1})^4$$
$$= (\sqrt{-1})^2(\sqrt{-1})^2 = -1 \times -1 = 1$$

and so on.

Here is an entertaining problem. We are asked to divide 10 into two parts such that their product is 40. Sounds easy, doesn't it? Let's try it.

On dividing 10 into two digits as shown below, the products become progressively larger until a maximum is reached when the ten is halved. The two digits are then equal and their product is a square, namely 25. Thus—

$$10 = 1 + 9 \quad \text{and} \quad 1 \times 9 = 9$$
$$2 + 8 \qquad\qquad 2 \times 8 = 16$$
$$3 + 7 \qquad\qquad 3 \times 7 = 21$$
$$4 + 6 \qquad\qquad 4 \times 6 = 24$$
$$5 + 5 \qquad\qquad 5 \times 5 = 25$$

Obviously we cannot mount any higher and the problem would appear to be insoluble. Some 400 years ago, however, Cardan showed that such was not the case. Any number $2x$ may be divided into two parts which we will denote by $x + y$ and $x - y$ respectively. Then clearly

$$(x + y) + (x - y) = 2x$$

Since

$$(x + y)(x - y) = x^2 - y^2$$

we may give a real value to x and an imaginary one to y. As y^2 must be real, $x^2 - y^2$ must also be real. Cardan therefore solved the problem by dividing 10 into the two numbers $5 + \sqrt{-15}$ and $5 - \sqrt{-15}$. The product of these is 40. Thus

$$(5 + \sqrt{-15})(5 - \sqrt{-15}) = 5^2 - (\sqrt{-15})^2$$
$$= 25 + 15 = 40$$

The Digital Root

To obtain the digital root of any particular integer, first sum up the digits, then sum up the digits of the number so obtained, and repeat this summation until only one digit remains. This is the digital root.*

* Dudeney, "Amusements in Mathematics" (Nelson) 1946, p. 13.

Thus, for example, take 43769. The sum of the digits is $4 + 3 + 7 + 6 + 9 = 29$; $2 + 9 = 11$; $1 + 1 = 2$—the digital root. We shall have occasion to refer to this many times in the sequel.

Perfect Numbers

A perfect number is one the sum of whose factors or divisors equals the number itself. In an imperfect number the sum of the divisors is less; in an over-perfect number it is greater.

As might be expected, perfect numbers are few and far between; so far as is known only even or female numbers can be perfect. This should please the ladies. Let us examine a few numbers for ourselves.

Number	Divisors	Sum of Divisors	Result
4	1, 2	3	Imperfect
5	1	1	Imperfect
6	1, 2, 3	6	Perfect
8	1, 2, 4	7	Imperfect
12	1, 2, 3, 4, 6	16	Overperfect
16	1, 2, 4, 8	15	Imperfect

and so on.

Only four other perfect numbers are known, namely, 28, 496, 8128 and 33,550,336, the last named being mentioned in an anonymous manuscript dating back to the middle of the 15th century.

Prime Numbers

A prime number is usually defined as an integer that has no divisors save 1 and itself. Numbers that have other divisors are termed composite. With the exception of 2, all primes are odd numbers and polydigital primes may end in 1, 3, 7 or 9, but not in 5, as all numbers ending in 5 are divisible by 5.

The Sieve of Eratosthenes

Eratosthenes, 274 to 194 B.C., one of the greatest scholars of the Alexandrian School, was known to his contemporaries as Beta, the second letter of the Greek alphabet. His admirers said that this was because he was a second Plato; others offered a more mundane explanation, namely that he occupied room 2 in the University. He invented what is known as the *Cribrum Arithmeticum* or Arithmetical Sieve, which is used in sorting out the primes. The method is as follows—

All the integral numbers are written down in order of increasing magnitude. The evens are now cancelled out except 2. We thus obtain—

1	2	3	5	7	9
11		13	15	17	19
21		23	25	27	29
31		33	35	37	39
41		43	45	47	49
51		53	55	57	59
61		63	65	67	69
71		73	75	77	79
81		83	85	87	89
91		93	95	97	99

and so on.

We now reject successively all numbers divisible by 3, 5 and 7, except these digits themselves. This means that we have also rejected all numbers divisible by 4, 6, 8, 9 or 10, as these are all divisible by 2 or 3. We are thus left with

1	2	3	5	7	
11	...	13	...	17	19
...	...	23	...	...	29
31	...	...	...	37	...
41	...	43	...	47	...
...	...	53	...	...	59
61	...	...	...	67	...
71	...	73	...	...	79
...	...	83	...	...	89
...	...	...	...	97	...

Obviously any number, less than 100, that is divisible by 11 or a higher number must also be divisible by one of the first ten numbers and has already been cancelled out. Consequently the above 26 integers are primes.

Between 1 and 1000 there are 169 primes and of these 16 are palindromes reading the same backwards as forwards, e.g. 11, 131, 373, etc. (p. 101). Between 1 and 10 million there are 664,580 primes; all the other numbers have been factorized.

Euler's Equation

Leonard Euler (1707–1783), a German who spent most of his life at St. Petersburg under the patronage of Catherine II, was one of the foremost mathematicians of his day. He showed that the expression

$$x^2 + x + 41$$

represents prime numbers when $x = 0, 1, 2, 3 \ldots$
up to 39. x may also have negative values. Thus

x	$x^2 + x + 41$	x	$x^2 + x + 41$
-5	61		
-2	43	2	47
-1	41	3	53
0	41	4	61
$+1$	43	5	71

and so on.

For $x = 40$, however, the expression gives 1681
which is 41^2.

The highest prime number known is

$$2^{127} - 1$$

Edouard Lucas of Paris (1842–1891) is said to have
spent 19 years in checking it. It was a gigantic task
for—$2^{127} - 1 = 170{,}141183{,}460469{,}231731{,}687303{,}$-
$715884{,}105727$ or approximately 170 hextillion
(British) or 170×10^{36}.

Classification of Primes

Primes may be divided into two classes, namely
$4n + 1$ and $4n - 1$. Two, the solitary even prime,
does not obey this rule.

But do not be misled. Although every prime may
be represented either as $4n + 1$ or $4n - 1$, not every
$4n + 1$ or $4n - 1$ is a prime.

For example, putting $n = 1, 2, 3 \ldots$.

n	$4n + 1$	$4n - 1$
2	9	7*
3	13*	11*
4	17*	15
5	21	19*
6	25	23*

and so on.

Of the above only the six starred numbers are prime, the others being composite.

Prime Curios

1. The following are primes—

$$19 \quad 109 \quad 1009 \quad 10009$$

No other digit can replace the 9 and yield four primes.

2. Primes are the only numbers which, when cubed, yield palindromes, that is, numbers reading the same backwards as forwards (p. 101). No composite number can do so. *E.g.*

$$11^3 = 1331$$

101

This is our lowest prime of three digits. If we wish to multiply any two-digit number by 101 we need not trouble to multiply out in the ordinary way. Why not? Well, let us see.

Suppose we multiply 23 by 101

$$
\begin{array}{r}
23 \\
101 \\
\hline
23 \\
23 \\
\hline
2323 \\
\end{array}
$$

All we need do, therefore, is to write the given number twice in succession. Hence any four-digit number comprising a two-digit number written twice in succession must be divisible by 101 and cannot therefore be a prime even if the original two-digit number, like 23, is a prime.

When squared, cubed, or raised to even higher powers, larger palindromes are produced (p. 104). It may be mentioned that 1001 is not a prime, for it is divisible by 7, 11 and 13 (p. 105).

Problems with Primes

Here are a few problems in which prime numbers are involved. Answers on p. 189.

1. TOM'S ADDRESS

Two former schoolmates met one day quite by accident on a bus. After exchanging greetings and inquiring about each other's health, family and prospects, Tom said "Look here, David, couldn't we meet somewhere and have a talk about old times? Could you by any chance come along and have dinner with us this evening? My wife Clara says she is always interested in meeting any one who is condescending enough to take any notice of me." "Delighted," was the reply, "but where can I find you?" "I live in Odd Street," said Tom, "so called, not because of the people, but because all the house numbers are odd. My number comprises three digits and is a perfect square. Moreover, if the number-plate were inverted it would show a prime number comprising the same three digits but arranged differently." "Thanks," said David, "I shall be along about seven. So long." And sure enough David turned up at the appointed time and the two friends spent a most enjoyable evening. By the way, what *was* the number of the house?

2. A FAMILY PROBLEM

Edward Prime was lunching with one of his colleagues in the late spring of 1951. "You know, Frank," he said "When I filled in our census form last year I noticed several curious coincidences. There were only three of us at home at the time, my wife, my son John and myself. It so happened that all our ages in years were primes and totalled 101. In six years' time they will all be primes again and my wife's age and mine will total up to 100. As I am slightly older than my wife it will not be difficult for you to work out our three ages." Frank made a few notes on the back of an envelope and then gave Edward the desired figures. What were they?

3. PAT AND MIKE

Two Irishmen, father and son, were celebrating their birthdays which both fell on the seventh day of the seventh month.

"Now I remember," said Pat, "that last year I was twice your age, my son."

"Aye, Dad, that's true," replied Mike, "but have ye noticed that both our ages are prime numbers?"

"Aye, lad, that I have," added Pat, "and, what is even more remarkable, your age is the exact reverse of mine."

What were their ages?

4. THE VILLAGE POSTMAN

Old John Stamp had been the village postman for forty years and was known and loved by all the villagers. He had had his ups and downs like many another and his only son's name figured on the war-memorial in the churchyard. He had given his life for his country, and it was left to John to bring up his only grandson, Charlie.

One morning John delivered a parcel at the rectory and the rector himself opened the door. "Ah, John, thank you," was the rector's genial greeting, "And how's Charlie? I haven't seen him at Sunday School lately. He's growing into a fine lad. How old might he be now?" "I doant rightly know" replied John with a twinkle in his eye, "but mebbe ye'll be able to reckon it out. It was only this morning as I was athinking that if my son had been alive, his age and

Charlie's and mine in years would have been what our schoolmaster used to call primes—ye'll know what they is, Sir—and would have added up to 99. Now Sir, last year my son would have been five times as old as Charlie. Good day, Sir." As John turned to continue his round the rector thought to himself—"he's a curious old man. I guess I can now find out the ages of all three." And he did. Could you?

5. THE FAIR TICKET

Mr. Cash plumped his money on the counter and received in exchange a ticket entitling him to enter the Fair Grounds.

"Interesting" he muttered to himself as he examined the number stamped on his ticket; "it has five different digits, the first pair and the last pair are squares, so is the middle digit, and it isn't one either. Then, too, the whole number is a square and, by Jove, its root is a prime number and a palindrome at that. I am sure this is unique."

Yes, Mr. Cash, it certainly is unique. Can the reader find out what the number of the ticket was?

Incommensurable Numbers

Incommensurable or irrational numbers are all such as cannot be completely expressed by an ordinary fraction. Al Khwarâzmi (p. 25) defined rational numbers as audible, and irrational as inaudible. As the Latin word *surdus* means deaf or insensible, inaudible numbers came to be known as surds.

That one incommensurable number exists was known to Pythagoras about 550 B.C., namely the ratio of the diagonal of a square to one of its sides. This we now call $\sqrt{2}$ and it is said that when the Greeks found this to be irrational they sacrificed 100 oxen to celebrate so important a discovery.

Figure 4

Other important incommensurables were discovered later.

The Edible Number

An incommensurable number of exceptional importance is that denoted by π, the Greek letter p, pronounced pie and sometimes humorously known as the edible letter or number.

As every schoolboy knows, the ratio of the circumference of a circle to its diameter gives a value for π. Thus

$$\pi = \frac{\text{circumference of circle}}{\text{diameter}}$$
$$\pi = 3.14159265358979323846264643383279$$

In Biblical times the circumference of a circle was taken as three times the diameter, and for the crude purposes of the ancients that was probably quite near enough. In I *Kings* 7: 23 we read of a bronze cauldron, described as a "molten sea" being made in connection with Solomon's Temple c.966 B.C. "ten cubits from the one brim to the other . . . and a line of thirty cubits did compass it round about." As a cubit was about 20 inches the making of the cauldron was no mean metallurgical achievement, the diameter being nearly 20 feet.

In the Middle Ages $\sqrt{10} = 3.162$ was often taken as a near approach to π and for rough calculations we today often take $\pi = 22/7 = 3.143$, which is nearer still.

The value 3.1416 is sufficiently accurate for even the most refined aircraft engineering work, its error being less than 1 in 300,000. Nevertheless, in 1430, π had been calculated to 16 places of decimals by Al Kashi, an Arabian mathematician. The German mathematician Ludolph van Ceulen (1540–1610) calculated π to 35 places of decimals, working on it almost to the day of his death. Long resident in Holland, he died in Leyden and his value for π was inscribed on his tombstone in St. Peter's Church. The Germans are wont to refer to π in consequence as the Ludolphian number.

In 1873 William Shanks evaluated π to 707 places of decimals—a truly prodigious feat; but was it really worth the trouble? I ask you because, like

Rosa Dartle of *David Copperfield* fame, "I want to know *so* much."

Mnemonics

Many mnemonics have been suggested to enable one to write down lengthy values for π, the number of letters in successive words giving successive digits. Two are as follows—

   1. English

     How I wish I could recollect pi easily today
      3 1 4 1 5   9 2 6   5

   2. French

     Que j'aime à faire connaître ce nombre
      3 1 4 1 5   9   2   6
     utile aux vrais amateurs Archimède
      5 3   5   8   9

The reference to Archimedes (287–212 B.C.) pays graceful tribute to that remarkable philosopher's genius in proving that π lies between $3\frac{1}{7}$ or 3.14286 and $3\frac{10}{71}$ or 3.14084. The mean of these two values, viz., 3.14185, differs by less than 1 part in 10,000 from that now accepted.

In 1951 Lord Balfour of Burleigh set a competition in "The Dark Horse"—the staff magazine of Lloyds Bank, the idea being to invent an English mnemonic that would serve the same purpose as the French. The winning contribution was as follows—

"Now I will a rhyme construct,	3.14159
By chosen words the young instruct,	265358
Cunningly devised endeavour,	979
Con it and remember ever	32384
Widths in circle here you see	626433
Sketched out in strange obscurity—"	83279

Another contribution, less lengthy but very true to life for many of us, ran—

"Now I live a drear existence in ragged suits
and cruel taxation suffering . . ."

Buffon's Needle Problem

Probably few of us ever think of π as representing anything other than the ratio of the circumference to the diameter of a circle. We learned it at school

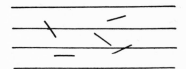

Figure 5. BUFFON'S NEEDLE EXPERIMENT

and it was never even hinted to us that π might have a wider significance. Actually π is an integral part of mathematics and crops up again, again and yet again.

Suppose we draw a series of parallel lines on a firm, flat surface, such as a table top, as in Fig. 5. distance l apart. If, now, we allow a needle of length l to drop at random from our hand onto the table, the chance that the needle will fall across one of the lines is $2/\pi$ times the chance that it will not. This remarkable observation was made by Count Buffon, the naturalist (1707–1788).

Lazzarini, an Italian mathematician, tested this observation in 1901 very fully. He made more than 3,400 tosses and obtained a value for $\pi = 3.1415929$, differing only by 1 in 10 million from the theoretical value. Perhaps you would like to try the experiment yourself and see what kind of a value you can obtain.

Coincidences

Here are two curious coincidences—

(I) The diameter of the Earth at the Equator is 7926.66 miles,

$$= 10^3 \sqrt{20 \times 3.1416}$$
$$= 10^3 \sqrt{20\pi} \text{ approximately}$$

(II)
$$\sqrt{51} - 4 = 3.1414$$
$$= \pi \text{ approximately}$$

V

THE OLD CURIOSITY SHOP

WHEN we visit an old curiosity shop we expect to find a more or less heterogeneous collection of curios and oddments, charms and talismans, that excite our interest and stimulate what in man is called thirst for knowledge, but in a woman mere curiosity. In the following pages the reader will find an amusing collection of arithmetical freaks and curiosities which will amply repay careful perusal.

THE DIGITS

Many of our words contain all the vowels once, but only three common ones have them in alphabetical order; these are *Abstemious*, *Arsenious* and *Facetious*.

Similarly many arithmetical expressions have been devised containing all the digits, a few of them having the digits in progressive order.

1. Here are nine equations each containing nine digits 1 to 9 once—

$$4 \times 1738 = 6952 \qquad 12 \times 483 = 5796$$
$$4 \times 1963 = 7852 \qquad 42 \times 138 = 5796$$

$$18 \times 297 = 5346 \qquad 28 \times 157 = 4396$$
$$27 \times 198 = 5346 \qquad 39 \times 186 = 7254$$
$$\qquad\qquad\qquad\qquad 48 \times 159 = 7632$$

2. Several other similar equations can be found if we include the cipher. Thus—

$$2 \times 3485 = 1 \times 6970 \qquad 3 \times 5694 = 17082$$
$$64 \times 915 = 80 \times 732 \qquad 27 \times 594 = 16038$$
$$78 \times 345 = 26910$$

3. The following double equation contains all the digits—

$$2 \times 78 = 156 = 4 \times 39$$

4. In these three equations all nine digits occur on each side—

$$51,249,876 \times 3 = 153,749,628$$
$$32,547,891 \times 6 = 195,287,346$$
$$16,583,742 \times 9 = 149,253,678$$

5. If we subtract the nine digits written in ascending order from the same in descending order, the result likewise contains all nine digits but arranged differently—

+	9	8	7	6	5	4	3	2	1
−	1	2	3	4	5	6	7	8	9
	8	6	4	1	9	7	5	3	2

6. When the nine digits are arranged in ascending order and multiplied by 2, 4, 5, 7 or 8, that is by digits that are not divisible by 3, the product contains all the digits but again arranged differently—

```
1 2 3 4 5 6 7 8 9 × 2 = 246,913,578
          ditto    × 4 = 493,827,156
          ditto    × 5 = 617,283,945
          ditto    × 7 = 864,197,523
          ditto    × 8 = 987,654,312
```

7. Here is a simple equation involving six different digits—

$$3839 \times 2 = 7678$$

The same digits can be arranged another way, namely—

$$2789 \times 3 = 8367$$

8. In the following expressions the products on the right are composed of the same digits as their factors on the left—

8 × 473 = 3784	21 × 87 = 1827
9 × 351 = 3159	27 × 81 = 2187
15 × 93 = 1395	35 × 41 = 1435
14 × 926 = 12964	78 × 624 = 48672
24 × 651 = 15624	87 × 435 = 37845
42 × 678 = 28476	72 × 936 = 67392
51 × 246 = 12546	65 × 281 = 18265
57 × 834 = 47538	65 × 983 = 63895
75 × 231 = 17325	86 × 251 = 21586

Reversals

9. It occasionally happens that a number, when multiplied by a digit, yields a product

composed of the original digits in reverse. Thus—

$$2178 \times 4 = 8712$$
$$1089 \times 9 = 9801$$

10. The curious will note that

$$362 - 236 = 14 \times 9$$

whereas

$$632 - 263 = 9 \times 41$$

11. The following equations are correct whether the digits are read as usual from left to right, or from right to left—

$112 \times 113 = 12656$	and	$65621 = 311 \times 211$
$112 \times 124 = 13888$	ditto	$88831 = 421 \times 211$
$112 \times 133 = 14896$	ditto	$69841 = 331 \times 211$
$112 \times 223 = 24976$	ditto	$67942 = 322 \times 211$
$122 \times 213 = 25986$	ditto	$68952 = 312 \times 221$

It is not difficult to find many others, and if the cipher be included the number may be very considerably increased.

Miscellaneous Oddities

12. We can express 100 as a product of two factors in which all the digits are involved. Thus—

$$(1 + 2 - 3 - 4)(5 - 6 - 7 - 8 - 9) = 100$$

13. The following three-digit numbers are each divisible by the product of their digits—

111	112	115	128	132	135	144
175	212	216	224	312	315	384
432	612	624	672	735	and	816

Thus taking 624, for example, we have $6 \times 2 \times 4 = 48$, and $624 \div 48 = 13$.

14. The following scheme is known as the *digital triangle*—

$$1 \times 8 + 1 = 9$$
$$12 \times 8 + 2 = 98$$
$$123 \times 8 + 3 = 987$$
$$1234 \times 8 + 4 = 9876$$

and so on until

$$123456789 \times 8 + 9 = 987654321$$

15. Is there anything unusual in the following sum of money?

£98,765   4s   3½d.

You say immediately that it contains all the digits. True, and it will be noted that this is the largest sum of money in English currency that can be written in this way. The smallest is

£2567   18s   9¾d.

Digital Fractions

16. The sums of the odd and even digits are 25 and 20 respectively, thus—

$$1 + 3 + 5 + 7 + 9 = 25$$
$$2 + 4 + 6 + 8 \quad = 20$$

The problem is to arrange the digits so that the sum of the odd ones is the same as that of the evens. This can be done if we are permitted to use fractions. Thus—

$$79 + 5\tfrac{1}{3} = 84\tfrac{1}{3} = 84 + \tfrac{2}{6}$$
$$\text{odd digits} \qquad\qquad \text{even digits}$$

17. It is possible to divide the nine digits into two groups such that one will divide into the other an integral number of times—in other words, without a remainder. Here a few examples; several others are known.

$$\frac{13458}{6729} = 2 \qquad \frac{15768}{3942} = 4 \qquad \frac{17658}{2943} = 6 \qquad \frac{25496}{3187} = 8$$

$$\frac{17469}{5823} = 3 \qquad \frac{13485}{2697} = 5 \qquad \frac{16758}{2394} = 7 \qquad \frac{57429}{6381} = 9$$

18. Here are four ways of expressing 5 as a fraction in which the denominator and numerator together contain all nine digits—

$$\frac{13485}{2697} = \frac{13845}{2769} = \frac{14865}{2973} = \frac{18645}{3729} = 5$$

19. In a similar manner we can express 9 in three different ways—

$$\frac{75249}{8361} = \frac{58239}{6471} = \frac{57429}{6381} = 9$$

20. Three more ways are possible if the cipher is included. Thus—

$$\frac{97524}{10836} = \frac{95823}{10647} = \frac{95742}{10638} = 9$$

21. The nine digits may be arranged in eleven different ways to represent 100. Thus—

$$3\,\frac{69258}{714} = 3 + 97 \qquad 91\,\frac{5742}{638} = 91 + 9$$

$$81\,\frac{5643}{297} = 81 + 19 \qquad 91\,\frac{5823}{647} = 91 + 9$$

$$81\,\frac{7524}{396} = 81 + 19 \qquad 91\,\frac{7524}{836} = 91 + 9$$

$$82\,\frac{3546}{197} = 82 + 18 \qquad 94\,\frac{1578}{263} = 94 + 6$$

$$96\,\frac{1428}{357} = 96 + 4$$

$$96\,\frac{1752}{438} = 96 + 4$$

$$96\,\frac{2148}{537} = 96 + 4$$

22. We are asked to arrange four 8's to represent respectively 1, 20, 26, 32, 88, 89, 98 and 880. At first sight this may appear to be impossible, but upon second thoughts we find the problem is capable of easy solution. Thus

$$\frac{88}{88} = 1 \qquad \frac{8}{.8} + \frac{8}{.8} = 20 \qquad 8 + 8 + \frac{8}{.8} = 26$$

and so on.

Analogous problems can be set with other digits. It is worth-while experimenting with four 1's. You will be surprised at what can be done.

23. Here is a problem that appears at first glance to be rather difficult, namely, to write down all the digits and the cipher in such a way that the expression is equal to unity. Two solutions readily suggest themselves. First we may write

$$\frac{2 \times 3485}{1 \times 6970} = 1$$

A second solution is based on the well-known fact that $x^0 = 1$, whatever the value of x, whence

$$123456789^0 = 1$$

The digits on the left may, of course, be arranged in any order, provided the cipher is used as the power index.

CURIOUS NUMBERS

9

This is a remarkable digit,—the smallest square of an odd number. The nine digits add up to 45 and $4 + 5 = 9$; moreover when nine is multiplied by any digit, the sum of the digits in the product is always nine. Thus—

$$9 \times 2 = 18 \quad \text{and} \quad 1 + 8 = 9$$
$$9 \times 3 = 27 \quad \text{ditto} \quad 2 + 7 = 9$$
$$9 \times 4 = 36 \quad \text{ditto} \quad 3 + 6 = 9$$

and so on.

Similarly if any number of two or more digits is multiplied by nine, the sum of the digits in the product is a multiple of nine. For example—

$$64 \times 9 = \quad 576 \qquad 5 + 7 + 6 = 18 = 9 \times 2$$
$$853 \times 9 = \quad 7677 \qquad 7 + 6 + 7 + 7 = 27 = 9 \times 3$$
$$7643 \times 9 = 68787 \qquad 6 + 8 + 7 + 8 + 7 = 36 = 9 \times 4$$

This is the principle of the well-known method of "casting out the nines." Any number, the sum of whose digits is 9 or a multiple of 9, must be divisible by 9.

For example, what digit must be put between 3 and 1 to make 7531628 divisible by 9? The sum of the digits is 32, and since 36 is divisible by 9, the required digit is 4. Moreover, the final number will be divisible by 9 wherever the 4 is placed. You may like to check these—

$$75341628 \div 9 = 8371292$$
$$47531628 \div 9 = 5281292$$
$$75316284 \div 9 = 8368476$$

If we take any number containing two or more different digits and rearrange the digits in any order we please, the difference between the two numbers is divisible by 9. For example—

$$43 - \quad 34 = \quad 9$$
$$632 - \quad 263 = 369 \ = 41 \times 9$$
$$8574 - 4587 = 3987 = 443 \times 9$$

If we wish to multiply any number by 9 it is often convenient to multiply by 10 and then subtract the original number. Thus—

$$58 \times 9 = \quad 58(10 - 1) = \quad 580 - \quad 58 = \quad 522$$
$$673 \times 9 = 673(10 - 1) = 6730 - 673 = 6057$$

Let us examine the effect of multiplying 99 consecutively by each of the digits. Thus—

$$99 \times 2 = 198$$
$$99 \times 3 = 297$$
$$99 \times 4 = 396$$
$$99 \times 5 = 495$$

and so on.

The digits appear in reversed sequence as the initial and final digits of the products.

Here is a useful thing to know about nine: when proving a column of figures in simple book-keeping, such as balancing your checkbook with the bank statement, if you find a discrepancy which is divisible by nine you can generally trace the mistake to a simple transposition of figures, such as 31 for 13, a slip of the pen which can be made only too easily.

37

When multiplied by 3 or a multiple of 3 up to 27, this number gives a product comprising three similar digits. Thus—

$$37 \times 3 = 111 \qquad 37 \times 18 = 666$$
$$\times 6 = 222 \qquad \times 21 = 777$$
$$\times 9 = 333 \qquad \times 24 = 888$$
$$\times 12 = 444 \qquad \times 27 = 999$$
$$\times 15 = 555 \qquad --$$

153

To begin with note that

$$153 = 3 \times 51$$

is a palindromic equation reading the same backwards as forwards. A second peculiarity is as follows—

$$153 = 1^3 + 5^3 + 3^3$$

1089

This curious number is a square, namely 33^2. It is also the difference of two squares, namely

$$65^2 - 56^2 = 33^2$$

When multiplied by 9 the product contains the digits in reverse (p. 66). Thus—

$$1089 \times 9 = 9801$$

But this is not all.

Here is an interesting exercise. Think of any number comprising three digits; in order to avoid negatives it is preferable to make the hundred digit larger than the first. Thus, selecting any three numbers at random, such as 584, 753 and 872, we carry out successively the following operations— reverse and subtract, again reverse and add.

	584	753	872
Reverse	485	357	278
Subtract	099	396	594
Reverse	990	693	495
Add	1089	1089	1089

No matter what digits we select the result is always the same. Indeed it is not difficult to prove alge-

braically that such must be the case. Let the three
digits be represented by a, b and c, respectively; then,
carrying out the above operations, we have

	a	b	c
Reverse	c	b	a
Subtract	$a - c - 1$	9	$10 + c - a$
Reverse	$10 + c - a$	9	$a - c - 1$
Add	9	(18)	9
that is	10	8	9

Obviously this must be true whatever digits are
assigned to a, b and c, provided only that a is not
equal to c.

9801

This is the reverse of 1089 and may be obtained
from it by multiplying by 9 as we have already seen.

$$1089 \times 9 = 9801$$

It has a peculiarity shared by only two other four-
digit numbers (p. 84), namely that its square root
is given by adding together the first and second pairs
of integers. Thus

$$\sqrt{9801} = 98 + 1 = 99$$

It is interesting to note that

$$9801 \times 9 = 88{,}209$$

and

$$\sqrt{88{,}209} = 88 + 209 = 297$$

142857

This is perhaps the most curious expression we have so far had occasion to consider. Let us multiply it by 3—

$$\begin{array}{r} 142857 \\ 3 \\ \hline 428571 \end{array}$$

All we have done is to transfer the initial 1 to the end, to follow immediately after 7. 285714 behaves similarly; thus $285714 \times 3 = 857142$. Now let us try multiplying by 5—

$$\begin{array}{r} 142857 \\ 5 \\ \hline 714285 \end{array}$$

This time we have succeeded in transferring the 7 from the back to the front position.

When we multiply by other digits, the product always contains the original digits. Thus—

$$142857 \times 2 = 285714$$
$$142857 \times 4 = 571428$$
$$142857 \times 6 = 857142$$

The reason is that we are dealing with the digits of a recurring decimal. If we divide 1 by 7 we obtain

$$\tfrac{1}{7} = 0.142857,142857,142857,142857 \cdots$$
$$= 0.1\dot{4}285\dot{7}$$

The expression 142857 repeats itself an infinite num-

ber of times as indicated by the dots over the 1 and the 7 in the second line.
Since

$$\tfrac{1}{7} \times 7 = 1$$

it will come as no surprise that

$$142857 \times 7 = 999,999$$

Two other well-known recurring decimals are

$$\tfrac{1}{13} = 0.\dot{0}7692\dot{3}$$

and

$$\tfrac{1}{17} = 0.\dot{0}588235294117647\dot{}$$

ABSURDITIES AND FALLACIES

We are all of us more or less intrigued by the ridiculous and the absurd. Mathematicians likewise enjoy their little absurdities and fallacies. Here are a few that will interest you.

1. To prove that $1 = 0$

This may be done in several ways. One usual method is as follows:

Let $x = 1$
then $x^2 = 1$
and $x - 1 = x^2 - 1 = (x + 1)(x - 1)$
Dividing by $x - 1$ we get
$1 = x + 1$
Whence $x = 0$

The fallacy is of course that $x - 1 = 0$ and we

may not therefore divide the third equation by $x - 1$ because

$$0 \times \text{any quantity} = 0$$

If we were permitted to divide by 0, obviously $1 = \%$ which again is absurd.
Nevertheless the results of summation of certain series appear to point to the same conclusion. Consider the series

$$1 - 1 + 1 - 1 + 1 - 1 + \cdots$$

By pairing differently we obtain

$$(1 - 1) + (1 - 1) + (1 - 1) + \cdots = 0$$

and

$$1 + (1 - 1) + (1 - 1) + \cdots = 1$$
$$\text{whence } 1 = 0$$

2. To prove that $3 = -2$

Let $a = 3$ and $b = 2$
Writing $a + b = c$

and multiplying both sides of the equation by $a + b$ we obtain

$$(a + b)(a + b) = c(a + b)$$
$$\text{Whence } a^2 + 2ab + b^2 = ac + bc$$
By rearranging the terms
$$a^2 + ab - ac = -ab - b^2 + bc$$
$$\text{or } a(a + b - c) = -b(a + b - c)$$
and dividing by $(a + b - c)$ we find
$$a = -b \text{ or } 3 = -2$$

3. To prove that $1 = 2$

Let a = b = any number you like.
Then $ab = b^2$
and $ab - b^2 = a^2 - b^2$
Whence $b(a - b) = (a + b)(a - b)$
Dividing by $a - b$, $b = a + b = 2b$
Whence $1 = 2$

4. To prove that $1 = -1$

Since $\sqrt{x} \times \sqrt{y} = \sqrt{xy}$
it follows that
$\sqrt{-1} \times \sqrt{-1} = \sqrt{(-1) \times (-1)} = \sqrt{1}$
Hence $(\sqrt{-1})^2 = \sqrt{1}$
and $-1 = 1$

If this were true it would follow that -1 could not be greater than 1. But we will now show that it is.

5. To prove that $-1 > 1$

Let a = b = 1 and c = d = -1
Then $ab = cd$
and $a/c = d/b$
as $a/c = \dfrac{1}{-1}$, $a > c$
as $a/c = d/b$, d must necessarily be $> b$;
but $d/b = \dfrac{-1}{1}$
Therefore $-1 > 1$

What nonsense, to be sure.

6. THE APPLES

Here is an old problem. A woman went to market carrying two baskets of apples each containing 300. In one basket the apples were of better quality than in the other, and she was asking a nickel each for them; the others she was prepared to sell at three for a dime.

On reaching her stall a farmer came along and, after passing as usual the time of day, he enquired as to what she had for sale. The woman explained and the farmer replied, "Very good. One basket has apples at 3 for 10¢ and the other at 2 for 10¢, that is an average of 5 for 20¢. Now 600 apples at 5 for 20¢ is $24.00. If you like I will buy the lot from you straight away at this figure."

"No thanks," said the canny country woman, "You be very kind but I can make more than that."

At the close of the day the woman had sold all her apples to various customers at the prices mentioned above, and found she had $25.00, which she accounted for as follows—

300 apples at 5¢ each = $15.00
300 apples at three for 10¢ = $10.00

She was thus $1.00 better off than she would have been had she accepted the farmer's offer. Yet his offer seemed fair enough. How did this come about? (Answer p. 189.)

7. The Field of Barley

The Home Guard squad had had a tiring day and were now marching back to HQ in the direction of the arrows shown in Fig. 6. They were

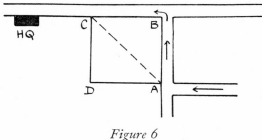

Figure 6

so tired that on reaching *A* they decided, at the risk of being fined for trespass, to cut across the square field of barley in the direction *AC* rather than tramp on the main road round *ABC*.

Captain Sharp, however, would not allow it, pointing to the harm that would be done to the crop. As the men grumbled he decided to pacify them. "What's all this fuss about?" he inquired, "You wouldn't gain anything by crossing the field; it is no further walking round by the road." Seeing the men didn't believe him he said, "Well, I'll prove it to you," and with his stick drew an outline of the field in the dust. "Look here," he said, "supposing I cut this side (*AB*) in two and draw *EF* parallel to *BC* and *FG* parallel to *AB* (Fig. 7a), it is obviously no further to walk along *AB* and *BC* than along *AE*, *EF*, *FG* and *GC*." The men grudgingly admitted this. Captain Sharp then divided each of the smaller sides into equal parts and connected up as shown in Fig. 7b and said, "You will, I am sure, agree that it is no further to walk along *AB* and *BC* than along *AH*, *HK*, *KL*, *LF*, *FM*, *MN*, *NP* and *PC*." After a little further thought the men agreed that this was

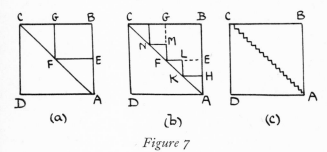

Figure 7

also correct. "Then," said the captain, "if we carry on in the same way until the zig-zags in the line *AC* are so small that we can afford to ignore them, it becomes obvious that to travel along *AB* and *BC* is no further than travelling along *AC* (Fig. 7c).

The argument appeared unanswerable; the men fell in obediently and marched to their HQ via *AB* and *BC*. All the same they felt that something was wrong. Their old schoolmaster, Mr. Spankemwell, had always taught them that two sides of a triangle were greater than the third. Was it possible that he was mistaken after all? What do you think about it?

8. Your Ancestors

Here is a curious problem. We may safely assume that you had two parents; each of your parents had two parents, so that you had four grandparents. Arguing along similar lines you must have had eight great grandparents and so on. Assuming an average of three generations per century the number of your ancestors since the Christian Era began must have been nearly 1 trillion—

$$1,000,000,000,000,000,000 \text{ or } 10^{18}$$

This is vastly more people than have ever lived on the Earth. What can we do about it?

9. Achilles and the Tortoise

This is an ancient problem, being propounded by Zeno, a Greek philosopher born at Elea c.496 B.C. He had studied the movements of bodies and asserted that, although it was contrary to experience, logical reasoning proved that a fast moving body could never overtake one moving more slowly if it had been given a preliminary start.

Being a Greek he naturally chose Achilles as representing a rapidly moving body, and it was easy to select the proverbially slow tortoise as the other body. If Achilles ran, say, ten times as rapidly as the tortoise and the latter was given a start of 1000 yards, we may assume that when Achilles began to run from A (Fig. 8), the tortoise was first leaving B. By the time Achilles reached B the tortoise had crawled to *C*, 100 yards further on. When Achilles reached *C*, the tortoise was 10 yards ahead at *D*, and so on, the tortoise always keeping ahead. It would appear, therefore, that although Achilles was always getting nearer to it he could never actually overtake the tortoise. But that was opposed

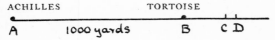

Figure 8. ACHILLES AND THE TORTOISE

to experience; where then was the catch? Apparently Zeno and his learned friends never succeeded in solving the problem. Let us see what we can make of it. The story really amounts to this—

Achilles runs the following distance

$$1000 + 100 + 10 + 1 + 0.1 + 0.01 + \cdots \text{ yards}$$

each successive addition becoming increasingly smaller as we progress.

This is what we call a converging series, that is to say, even when the series is extended to an infinite number of terms it never becomes indefinitely great. Indeed in this instance the maximum distance it can represent is ||||·|||| or ||||·| yards. What we have proved, therefore, by the above reasoning is that Achilles cannot overtake the tortoise within ||||·| yards. He will catch up to and pass the tortoise the moment the distance he has run exceeds ||||·| yards.

This is common sense and agrees with experience.

The same kind of problem has since been served up in a variety of forms. One common variant before the advent of motor buses, ran as follows—

A horse bus travels at the rate of 8 miles per hour; a man is given an hour's start and walks at 4 miles per hour. It was argued that the bus could never overtake the man.

From what has been said above it will be obvious that all that the argument proves is that the bus cannot overtake the man in fewer than two hours. It will catch up to him in two hours and will then pass him.

VI

THE POWERS THAT BE

SQUARES

Off with their Heads!

So SPAKE the enraged Queen of Hearts to the horror of little Alice in Wonderland; but Alice soon observed that these executions were bloodless and were not to be unduly worried about.

Let us carry out a few similarly harmless decapitations, this time with words. The following story is told of the late Sir Archibald Geikie, the famous British geologist. His assistant had written on the board a notice to the effect that the professor would meet his CLASSES at a given time, say 3:00 P.M. A wag deleted the C and the notice thus appeared to read that the professor would meet his LASSES at the appointed time. But Geikie himself happened to pass and observe the heresy, whereupon he promptly turned the tables by deleting the L. With roars of laughter the students now read that their professor would meet his ASSES at 3:00 P.M.

Unfortunately, like many another good story, this one doesn't happen to be true. When asked about it Sir Archibald denied its authenticity and, with a twinkle in his eye, added that he only wished it *were* true.

It is not difficult to find many other words that

can be beheaded twice or even three times to yield fresh ones. Prelate is unusual; it can be beheaded four times. Thus—

Prelate, Relate, Elate, Late, Ate.

Can we do anything analogous with numbers? Are there, for example, any properties that a number might be able to retain when beheaded?

Indeed, yes. One such is what we may term "being on the square." For example 275,625 is the square of 525; when beheaded it yields 75,625 which is the square of 275. This beheading can be done in all four times. Thus—

$$275{,}625 = 525^2$$
$$75{,}625 = 275^2$$
$$5{,}625 = 75^2$$
$$625 = 25^2$$
$$25 = 5^2$$

This is the only number of six digits that can be beheaded four times in this way; it corresponds to the word prelate given above.

Rearrangements

By rearranging the letters in certain words it is often possible to produce other words. For example—

Now........... Own, Won
Name.......... Amen, Mane, Mean
Traces......... Caters, Crates, Reacts, Recast

In a similar manner the digits of many squares can

be rearranged to yield other squares. A few examples
are as follows—

$169 = 13^2$	$196 = 14^2$	$961 = 31^2$
$1296 = 36^2$	$2916 = 54^2$	$9216 = 96^2$
$11664 = 108^2$	$16641 = 129^2$	$41616 = 204^2$
$23716 = 154^2$	$32761 = 181^2$	$72361 = 269^2$
$36481 = 191^2$	$38416 = 196^2$	$43681 = 209^2$
$42849 = 207^2$	$49284 = 222^2$	$82944 = 288^2$

A Useful Observation

25 and 76 are the only two pairs of digits in the
first and second places of a number that reappear
when that number is squared, cubed, or raised to a
higher power. Here are a few examples—

$25^2 =$	$6\underline{25}$	$76^2 =$	$5,7\underline{76}$
$325^2 = 105,6\underline{25}$		$376^2 =$	$141,3\underline{76}$
$25^3 = 15,6\underline{25}$		$76^3 =$	$438,9\underline{76}$
$25^4 = 390,6\underline{25}$		$76^4 = 33,362,1\underline{76}$

In consequence of this—
  (1) The only two numbers that are the squares
      of their first and second digits are

$$625 = 25^2$$
$$5776 = 76^2$$

  (2) The only two numbers that are the squares
      of their first, second and third digits are

$$141,376 = 376^2$$
$$390,625 = 625^2$$

Reversals

It sometimes happens that square numbers upon reversal yield other squares. Occasionally this affords an easy method of squaring a number—so simple that you feel compelled to ask where the catch can be.

Take the number 21; to find its square all that we have to do is to reverse it obtaining 12. Now everybody knows that the square of 12 is 144. If then we reverse this latter number we obtain the square of 21, namely 441.

We may therefore write

$$12^2 = 12 \times 12 = 144$$
$$21^2 = 21 \times 21 = 441$$

Simple, isn't it? But will it always work? Let's try again, this time taking 31. Its reverse is 13, the square of which is 169; the square of 31, therefore, should be 961—and it is, too.

Unfortunately these are the only two-digit numbers that behave in this way. There are, however, many higher numbers that behave similarly, and if the cipher is permitted the list may be considerably extended.

$112^2 = 12544$	and	$211^2 = 44521$
$113^2 = 12769$	"	$311^2 = 96721$
$122^2 = 14884$	"	$221^2 = 48841$
$1112^2 = 1236544$	"	$2111^2 = 4456321$
$1113^2 = 1238769$	"	$3111^2 = 9678321$
$1121^2 = 1256641$	"	$1211^2 = 1466521$
$1212^2 = 1468944$	"	$2121^2 = 4498641$

Freaks and Curiosities

1. Here is a curious coincidence—

$$2^5 \times 9^2 = 2592$$

2. The numbers 48 and 1680 are unique in that the addition of 1 to them and to their halves renders them perfect squares. Thus—

$$48 + 1 = 49 = 7^2 \qquad 1680 + 1 = 1681 = 41^2$$
$$48\tfrac{1}{2} + 1 = 25 = 5^2 \qquad 1680\tfrac{1}{2} + 1 = 841 = 29^2$$

It will be noted that all the squares are those of primes.

3. The following numbers are peculiar in that each is exactly divisible not merely by the sum of its digits but also by the square of the sum of its digits.

162, 243, 324, 392, 512, 648, 972.
1296, 2156, 2916, 3564, 4536, 5184, 5632, 5832.
7128, 7452

Thus, for example, take 392—

$$3 + 9 + 2 = 14; \qquad 14^2 = 196; \qquad 392 \div 196 = 2$$

4. It is worth noting that

$$10 = 1^2 + 3^2 \qquad 10,000 = 28^2 + 96^2$$
$$100 = 8^2 + 6^2 \qquad 100,000 = 12^2 + 316^2$$
$$1000 = 18^2 + 26^2 \qquad 1,000,000 = 352^2 + 936^2$$

Also, while $10 = 1 + 2 + 3 + 4$
$$100 = (1 + 2 + 3 + 4)^2$$

PYTHAGOREAN SQUARES

It frequently happens that the sum of two squares is itself a square; in other words there are many solutions to the equation

$$x^2 + y^2 = z^2$$

where x, y and z represent integers. Here are a few examples—

$$3^2 + 4^2 = 5^2 \qquad 7^2 + 24^2 = 25^2$$
$$5^2 + 12^2 = 13^2 \qquad 8^2 + 15^2 = 17^2$$
$$6^2 + 8^2 = 10^2 \qquad 9^2 + 40^2 = 41^2$$

There are many others; they are known as Pythagorean Squares because Pythagoras is usually credited with having proved that the square on the hypotenuse of a right-angled triangle equals the

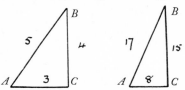

Figure 9. RIGHT-ANGLED TRIANGLES

sum of the squares on the other two sides. If therefore we draw triangles with sides proportional in length to the numbers in each of the above equations, the angles opposite the longest sides will be right angles. Thus, for example, in each of the triangles in Fig. 9

$$AB^2 = AC^2 + BC^2$$

and the angle ACB is a right angle. In general

we may write $(n^2 + 1)^2 = (2n)^2 + (n^2 - 1)^2$ where n is any integer.

The Problem of the Rolling Log

A boy jumped onto one end of a piece of tree trunk lying on the top of a hill. Now the log happened to be exactly 13 feet long, an unlucky omen for the youth, and the impact caused it to begin rolling down the hill. As it rolled, he managed to keep himself upright on top and slowly walked across the log to the other end which he reached just as the log came to rest at the bottom of the hill, 84 feet from where it began to roll.

The log was 2 feet in diameter. How far did the boy actually travel and how far would he have travelled had the log been 3 feet in diameter? The answer is given on p. 189.

It is worth noting that, as we can write the equation

$$x^2 + y^2 = z^2$$

in the form

$$x^2 = z^2 - y^2$$

it follows that every square may be expressed as the difference between two squares. The following example is of special interest because the numbers on each side may be reversed—

$$33^2 = 65^2 - 56^2$$

Even more interesting are the following four equations, the numbers in which may also be read in the reverse direction—

$$41^2 - 14^2 = 87^2 - 78^2$$
$$51^2 - 15^2 = 75^2 - 57^2$$
$$62^2 - 26^2 = 97^2 - 79^2$$
$$72^2 - 27^2 = 96^2 - 69^2$$

Hoppenot's Rule

The sum of the squares of $n + 1$ consecutive integers, of which the greatest is $2n(n + 1)$, equals the sum of the squares of the next n integers.

The simplest case is when $n = 1$; then $2n(n + 1) = 4$ and consequently

$$3^2 + 4^2 = 5^2$$

which was our first example.

When $n = 2$, $2n(n + 1) = 12$ and
$$10^2 + 11^2 + 12^2 = 13^2 + 14^2$$

and so on.

SQUARE ROOTS

1. Most of us look upon the usual arithmetical method of evaluating square roots of numbers as cumbersome. Here is a dodge worth knowing; it consists in dividing the number into two parts and adding the parts together. The sum gives us the square root of the original number. Here are a few examples—

$$\sqrt{81} = 8 + 1 = 9 \qquad \sqrt{88,209} = 88 + 209 = 297$$
$$\sqrt{2025} = 20 + 25 = 45 \qquad \sqrt{494,209} = 494 + 209 = 703$$
$$\sqrt{3025} = 30 + 25 = 55 \qquad \sqrt{998,001} = 998 + 1 = 999$$
$$\sqrt{9801} = 98 + 1 = 99$$

Nothing could be simpler. Then why weren't we taught this simple rule at school? Because it so happens that the above are the only seven numbers less than one million that behave in this way.

2. The square roots of two numbers, 6561 and 8281, may be obtained by summing up the digits and reversing. Thus—

$$6561 \ldots 6 + 5 + 6 + 1 = 18 \qquad 81 = \sqrt{6561}$$
$$8281 \ldots 8 + 2 + 8 + 1 = 19 \qquad 91 = \sqrt{8281}$$

3. 784 is unique in that its square root is the product of its first and last digits—

$$\sqrt{784} = 7 \times 4 = 28$$

CUBES

The equation

$$x^2 + y^2 = z^2$$

is a special case of the general equation

$$x^n + y^n = z^n$$

where $n = 2$.

Pierre de Fermat, the famous French mathematician (1601–1665), stated that this general equation is only true when $n = 2$ if n is an integer and greater than 1. This is known as *Fermat's Last Theorem* and is believed to be true although it does not appear to have been proved; it has, however, been tested up to $n = 617$ and found to hold good.

As there is no solution in integers for the expression

$$x^3 + y^3 = z^3$$

it follows that a given cube cannot be cut down into two smaller cubes such that the length of their sides shall be exact integers. It is of course easily possible to prepare from a given cube two smaller ones, the combined volumes of which shall differ by as little as we please from the volume of the original cube, but the sides of both cubes can never be exact integers although the sides of one may be.

For example, a cube of edge 12 inches and volume 12^3 or 1728 cubic inches can be divided into two cubes, one of edge, say, 10 inches and volume 1000 cubic inches; the other cube should theoretically have a volume of 728 inches. But $\sqrt[3]{728}$ is incommensurable, namely 8.99588 . . . inches, so that we can never prepare a cube of exactly 728 cubic inches, although we can approach as nearly as we please to this value, namely 727.999 . . . .

Apollo's Problem

According to an ancient Greek legend, the Athenians in 430 B.C. suffered from a severe plague and, as usual in such circumstances, consulted the oracle at Delos in the hope of finding a remedy. The god, Apollo, graciously said that if they doubled the size of his cubical altar all would be well.

Delighted at so easy a remedy a new altar was quickly built having each of its edges doubled in length. But the plague persisted; it became even more virulent; evidently Apollo was not pleased. The Athenians therefore invoked the oracle a second time and were informed that Apollo was indeed angry; the stupid builders had not doubled the size of his altar, they had increased it eight-fold.

The problem was of course theoretically insoluble. But a cubic altar could easily have been constructed differing from twice the size of the existing one by as minute an amount as the exactness of building science would permit. Obviously if l was the length of the edge of Apollo's existing altar, and x the required edge-length of the new one,

$$2l^3 = x^3 \qquad \text{or} \qquad x = l \times \sqrt[3]{2}$$

Although $\sqrt[3]{2}$ is incommensurable, it is easy enough to evaluate it with an accuracy far beyond the practical attainment of any builder, for

$$x = 1.25992 \ldots \times l$$

The oracles generally worked in some such ambiguous way as this because the priests had to leave an avenue for "face-saving" in case their advice went astray. If the people once lost confidence in the oracles the income of the attendant priests would be lost forever. If in the ordinary run of nature the plague had decreased in violence after the erection of the 8-fold altar, the oracle would have been regarded as fulfilled, and it would not have been necessary for Apollo to discover that his instructions had not been properly carried out.

An Arab variant of the story says that it was the Children of Israel who suffered from the plague and that a voice from heaven proclaimed "Let the size of the altar be doubled and the plague will cease."

The Hebrews thought they had solved the problem by building a second altar of exactly the same dimensions as the first and placing the two side by side. But the plague did not subside and the divine powers found it necessary to find fault with even this arrangement.

Square Curios

1. Although the equation $x^3 + y^3 = z^3$ cannot be solved with integral values for x and y, the longer expression

$$x^3 + y^3 + z^3 = w^3$$

admits of solution. Perhaps three of the simplest cases are

$$3^3 + 4^3 + 5^3 = 6^3$$
$$1^3 + 6^3 + 8^3 = 9^3$$
$$6^3 + 8^3 + 10^3 = 12^3$$

2. Other more complex expressions are—

$$1^3 + 5^3 + 7^3 + 12^3 = 13^3$$
$$2^3 + 3^3 + 8^3 + 13^3 = 14^3$$
$$1^3 + 2^3 + 7^3 + 10^3 + 14^3 = 16^3$$

3. Four three-digit numbers are equal in magnitude to the sum of the cubes of their individual digits, namely—

$$153 = 1^3 + 5^3 + 3^3$$
$$370 = 3^3 + 7^3 + 0^3$$
$$371 = 3^3 + 7^3 + 1^3$$
$$407 = 4^3 + 0^3 + 7^3$$

4. 1729 is unique in that it is the smallest integer that can be expressed in two ways as the sum of two different cubes. Thus

$$1729 = 1728 + 1 \text{ or } 12^3 + 1^3$$
$$= 1000 + 729 \text{ or } 10^3 + 9^3$$

5. It may be noted that

$$10 = 1 + 2 + 3 + 4$$
$$\text{but } 100 = 1^3 + 2^3 + 3^3 + 4^3$$

6. The only digit to yield a square when its cube is added to its divisors is 7. Thus

$$7^3 + (1 + 7 + 7^2) = 400 = 20^2$$

7. 1, 2 and 5 are the only three digits that can be arranged to yield two cubes. Thus—

$$125 = 5^3 \quad \text{and} \quad 512 = 8^3$$

CUBE ROOTS

1. The extraction of a cube root by arithmetical means is extremely cumbersome. The cube roots of five numbers are readily obtained by summing up their digits. Thus—

$$\sqrt[3]{512} = 5 + 1 + 2 = 8$$
$$\sqrt[3]{4913} = 4 + 9 + 1 + 3 = 17$$
$$\sqrt[3]{5832} = 5 + 8 + 3 + 2 = 18$$
$$\sqrt[3]{17576} = 1 + 7 + 5 + 7 + 6 = 26$$
$$\sqrt[3]{19683} = 1 + 9 + 6 + 8 + 3 = 27$$

2. The cube roots of five numbers only, each less than one million, are given by the reversal of the sum of their digits. Thus—

148,877	sum of digits 35	cube root 53
238,328	26	62
373,248	27	72
531,441	18	81
551,368	28	82

3. The cube roots of three numbers each less than one million may be obtained by multiplying together their first and last digits. Thus—

$$\sqrt[3]{125} = 1 \times 5 = 5$$
$$\sqrt[3]{3375} = 3 \times 5 = 15$$
$$\sqrt[3]{91,125} = 9 \times 5 = 45$$

HIGHER POWERS

1. What is the largest number obtainable with four 1's? If you are like most people you will probably say 1111. Well, let us see what we can do. First let us try adding—

$$1 + 1 + 1 + 1 = 4$$
$$11 + 11 = 22$$
$$111 + 1 = 112$$
$$1111 = 1111$$

This is the limit so far as simple addition is concerned. Now let us try powers—

$$1^{111} = 1$$
$$111^1 = 111$$

but

$$11^{11} = 285,311,670,611$$

You did not, I am sure, anticipate this.

2. Now what can we do with three 2's? We have a choice of four possibilities, namely

$$222$$
$$22^2 = 484$$
$$2^{2^2} = 2^4 = 16$$
$$2^{22} = 4,194,304$$

3. Similarly with three 3's we have

$$333$$
$$33^3 = 35,937$$
$$3^{3^3} = 3^{27}$$
$$3^{33}$$

As 3^{27} is less than 3^{33}, obviously this latter is the largest number obtainable with three 3's.

4. With three 4's however, the result is different. We may write

$$444$$
$$44^4 = 3,748,096$$
$$4^{44}$$
$$4^{4^4} = 4^{256}$$

It is evident that 4^{4^4} is by far the greatest number.

5. Finally, let us try three 9's. We have, of course, a similar choice, namely

$$999$$
$$99^9$$
$$9^{99}$$
$$9^{9^9} = 9^{387420489}$$

Obviously the last number is overwhelmingly the greatest. It has never been worked out. It has been calculated,* however, that if this number were written on a ribbon of paper, with 200 digits to each foot, some 350 miles of ribbon would be required. If a scribe undertook to write it down nonstop at the rate of two digits a second, he would require five years and 10 months to finish his task. The number begins with 428,124,773 . . . and ends with 89. Few of us will worry about the intermediate digits.

The Googal and Googalplex

Dr. Kasner of Columbia University has given the name Googal to 10^{100}. He says that the word was invented by his nine-year old nephew. If written in full it is 1 followed by 100 ciphers—

10,000,000,000,000,000,000,000,000,000,000,000
000,000,000,000,000,000,000,000,000,000,000,000
000,000,000,000,000,000,000,000,000,000,000,000

* Bakst, "Mathematics, Its Magic and Mastery," (New York, 1941), p. 61.

This is an enormous number, greater than any in common use in mathematics, physics or even astronomy. Great as it is, it is not infinitely great. A much greater number is the googalplex, that is 10 to the googal power, which may be written either as

$$10^{googal} \qquad \text{or} \qquad 10^{10^{100}}$$

Even this vast number is no nearer infinity than the googal itself. So perhaps it will be as well to let the matter rest here.

VII

SQUARES,

MAGIC AND OTHERWISE

MUCH pleasure may be derived from constructing word squares in which given words repeat themselves as the letters are read in horizontal and vertical columns in either direction. The small squares occupied by the letters are known as cells, and if *n* such cells occur in a row, the full square is of the *n*th order.

There is little scope with squares of the second and third order; it is easy to compile examples of the fourth, but much more difficult to compile one of the fifth order. The most famous of these is that constructed from the Latin palindrome, SATOR AREPO TENET OPERA ROTAS found scratched on

S	A	T	O	R
A	R	E	P	O
T	E	N	E	T
O	P	E	R	A
R	O	T	A	S

Figure 10

a fragment of wall plaster from a Roman villa at Cirencester, England. A suitable translation would appear to be—

The mechanic Arepo guides the wheels at work.

The word *sator* referred primarily to a sower and is usually translated as such. Poetically it was also used to denote a father, begetter or producer. In palindromes as in poetry, in order to make sense considerable license is given to the use of words, and the above translation probably represents fairly accurately what was intended, as a mechanic is usually a producer.

The palindrome is repeated in whichever direction we read, whether upwards or downwards, across or in reverse, but not diagonally.

NUMBER SQUARES

Numbers may be arranged in squares in such a manner that, while no two cells contain the same digit, the arrangement conforms to some specified rule.

In the following schemes the digits are arranged in such a manner that the second line is double the first and the third line is their sum and hence treble the first line.

First row	2 7 3	3 2 7	1 9 2	2 1 9
" × 2	5 4 6	6 5 4	3 8 4	4 3 8
" × 3	8 1 9	9 8 1	5 7 6	6 5 7

Figure 11

When the digits are arranged as in Fig. 12, each horizontal row is the square of a number.

3	6	1	19^2
5	2	9	23^2
7	8	4	28^2

Figure 12

MAGIC SQUARES

The squares so far discussed are not true magic squares; to be magical the sum of the numbers in each horizontal and vertical row, as well as in the two diagonals, must be the same.

The Lo Shu

Probably the most ancient magic square is one of the third order derived from the nine digits as shown in Fig. 13. As the digits add up to 45 they can be arranged in three rows of three cells each such that

8	3	4
1	5	9
6	7	2

Figure 13. THE LO SHU

their sums are 15, including the diagonals also. This square is known as the Lo Shu and dates back to the time of the Chinese Emperor Yü or Ta-Yü, that is Yü the Great, who reigned 2205 to 2198 B.C. The story goes that the Emperor stood, one day, on the banks of the Hoang Ho or the Yellow River gazing at its colored waters as they flowed beneath his feet; and lo, from their muddy depths there climbed out onto the bank a sacred tortoise bearing the strange device shown in Fig. 14. The numbers were figurate, that is, expressed by simple patterns of lines, dots and circles.

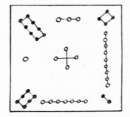

Figure 14. THE LO SHU IN CHINESE FIGURATE NUMBERS

It will be noted that all the odd or male digits lie within the cross (fig. 13) now recognized as that of St. George. In other words the cross contains the essence of masculinity and was in consequence regarded as the emblem of deity. The Lo Shu thus acquired a deep mystic significance and is held in the highest veneration in the East. It provides protection against the Evil Eye; placed over the entrance to a dwelling nothing evil can enter. Every fortune-teller in the East uses it. As a charm it is found inscribed in fortune bowls, medicine cups, on amulets and the like. He who would enjoy good health and the good things of life bears the Lo Shu on his person.

Eight varieties of the above scheme are possible by rotations and reflections; the central number, however, is always five and each row and diagonal always adds up to 15.

Magic Squares of the Fourth Order

These are more difficult to construct. Dürer's Square is shown in Fig. 15. It appears on one of his

16	3	2	13
5	10	11	8
9	6	7	12
4	15	14	1

Figure 15. DÜRER'S MAGIC SQUARE

engravings, *Melancholia*, and carries the date 1514 in the centre of the bottom row. It was one of the earliest magic squares of the fourth order to be printed; the numbers in the square may be arranged in several hundred ways and add up to 34 in every direction.

Magic squares of the fifth order have also been constructed.

Prime Squares

Magic squares have been constructed with prime numbers. Two are shown in Fig. 16 adding up to 111 and 102 respectively.

67	1	43
13	37	61
31	73	7

3	71	5	23
53	11	37	1
17	13	41	31
29	7	19	47

DUDENEY'S SQUARE

BERGHOLT AND
SHULDHAM'S SQUARE

Figure 16. MAGIC SQUARES OF PRIMES

Reversible Squares

The numbers in the one square in Fig. 17 are reversed in the other. Furthermore in each case the first place digits in every row or diagonal add up to 22, and the total numbers to 242.

15	96	93	38
94	37	16	95
36	91	98	17
97	18	35	92

83	39	69	51
59	61	73	49
71	89	19	63
29	53	81	79

Figure 17. REVERSIBLE MAGIC SQUARES

Magic Cubes

Magic cubes have been constructed, the simplest of which comprise the numbers 1 to 3^3. Three horizontal slices of such a cube are shown in Fig. 18—

18	23	1
22	3	17
2	16	24

20	7	15
9	14	19
13	21	8

4	12	26
11	25	6
27	5	10

Figure 18. THE MAGIC CUBE

When these slices are placed on top of each other, the sum of the numbers in each horizontal row and vertical column, as also in each of the four diagonals, is 42.

VIII

PALINDROMES

A GOOD many words read the same backwards as forwards, such as noon, madam, and so on. They are termed palindromes.* Palindromic sentences have also been constructed, though the words themselves are not of necessity palindromes. Thus Adam is supposed to have introduced himself to Eve with the words, in English mark you—

MADAM I'M ADAM

Napoleon, sullenly brooding over his fall as he disconsolately paced the shores of Elba, is said to have lamented, likewise in English—

ABLE WAS I ERE I SAW ELBA

By far the most important of all palindromes is the Latin one, to which reference has already been made (p. 94)—

SATOR AREPO TENET OPERA ROTAS

In a similar manner numerical expressions may be written down which read the same backwards as forwards.

* Greek *palin* backwards, *dromos* running.

1. Simple palindromes may often be obtained by adding a two-digit number to its reversal. Thus—

$$16 + 61 = 77 \qquad 35 + 53 = 88$$
$$24 + 42 = 66 \qquad 38 + 83 = 121$$

121 is exceptional for usually when the sum is a three digit number it is not palindromic. But if the process be repeated one or more times a palindromic sum may eventually be obtained. For example

$$68 + 86 = 154; \qquad 154 + 451 = 605;$$
$$605 + 506 = 1111$$

2. Sixteen of the 99 palindromes between 1 and 1000 are primes. These are

11, 101, 131, 151, 181, 191, 313, 353, 373, 383, 727, 757, 787, 797, 919, 929.

Power Palindromes

1. Eleven of the thousands of palindromes between 1 and 1,000,000 are squares. Of these seven are squares of palindromes, namely—

$$121 = 11^2 \qquad 14641 = 121^2$$
$$484 = 22^2 \qquad 40804 = 202^2$$
$$10201 = 101^2 \qquad 44944 = 212^2$$
$$12321 = 111^2$$

The other four squares are

$$676 = 26^2 \qquad 94249 = 307^2$$
$$69696 = 264^2 \qquad 698896 = 836^2$$

2. Many palindromes are the differences between two squares; in some cases the relationships are reversible. Thus—

$$2772 = 86^2 - 68^2$$
$$5445 = 83^2 - 38^2$$
$$6336 = 80^2 - 08^2$$

3. There are but two cubic palindromes less than one million, namely—

$$343 = 7^3 \quad \text{and} \quad 1331 = 11^3$$

The next highest cubic palindrome is

$$1030301 = 101^3$$

4. The only fourth power palindrome less than one million is

$$14641 = 11^4$$

There is no fifth power palindrome less than 10 million.

5. Eleven is unique in that its second, third and fourth powers are palindromes.

$$11$$
$$11^2 = 121$$
$$11^3 = 1331$$
$$11^4 = 14641$$

But higher powers are not palindromes. Thus—

$$11^5 = 161051$$

Products

1. The following expressions are palindromic as a whole—

$$3 \times 51 = 153$$
$$6 \times 21 = 126$$
$$8 \times 86 = 688$$

$12 \times 42 = 24 \times 21$	$21 \times 36 = 63 \times 12$
$13 \times 62 = 26 \times 31$	$23 \times 64 = 46 \times 32$
$14 \times 82 = 28 \times 41$	$24 \times 84 = 48 \times 42$

2. In the following expressions the separate integers are palindromes and the equations are therefore reversible although not themselves palindromic as a whole.

$111 \times 111 = 12321$	$121 \times 121 = 14641$
$111 \times 121 = 13431$	$121 \times 212 = 25652$
$111 \times 131 = 14541$	$121 \times 222 = 26862$
	$212 \times 141 = 29892$
and so on to	$212 \times 212 = 44944$
$111 \times 171 = 18981$	

The reader can easily find several more, and if the cipher is permitted the number may be very considerably increased.

101

This is the smallest three-digit palindrome. It is a prime and yields palindromic powers. Thus—

$$101^2 = 10201$$
$$101^3 = 1030301$$
$$101^4 = 104040401$$

and so on.

It not only reads the same backwards as forwards, but upside down and when reflected in a mirror.

595

To students of Holy Writ this palindrome has an interesting significance. The Bible has 1189 chapters counting each psalm as one. The middle chapter is obviously number 595, which is Psalm 117—not only the shortest psalm but the shortest of all the chapters in the Bible.

1001

Unlike 101, this is not a prime number for

$$1001 = 7 \times 11 \times 13$$

It is probably the world's most famous numerical palindrome for who has not heard of "The Thousand and One Nights," commonly called "The Arabian Nights' Entertainments"?

In the common expression "I have a thousand and one things to do" the number ceases to be specific and means simply an indefinite, large number.

Like 101, when squared, cubed or raised to a higher power, 1001 yields other palindromes. Thus—

$$1001^2 = 1002001$$
$$1001^3 = 1003003001$$

and so on.

69696

This is the product of two palindromes. Thus—

$$69696 = 6336 \times 11$$

6336 is unusual in that

$$6336 = 8 \times (63 + 36) \times 8$$

Palindromes of Like Digits

Expressions obtained by placing two or more ones together are interesting. Themselves monodigital palindromes, they are square roots of polydigitals.

The first of these, 11, is a prime number, its sole divisor being 1; it is the square root of 121. Each of the higher monodigital palindromes given below, however, has divisors and is the square root of a polydigital palindrome.

$$111 = 3 \times 37^* \qquad = \sqrt{12321}$$
$$1,111 = 11 \times 101 \qquad = \sqrt{1234321}$$
$$11,111 = 41 \times 271 \qquad = \sqrt{123454321}$$
$$111,111 = 3 \times 7 \times 11 \times 13 \times 37$$
$$= \sqrt{12345654321}$$
$$1,111,111 = 239 \times 4649 \qquad = \sqrt{1234567654321}$$
$$11,111,111 = 11 \times 73 \times 101 \times 137$$
$$= \sqrt{123456787654321}$$
$$111,111,111 = 9 \times 37 \times 333,667$$
$$= \sqrt{12345678987654321}$$

and so on.

The two numbers indicated by 17 and 18 successive ones respectively have two and eight divisors, namely—

* Palindromes obtained by multiplying 37 by 3 and multiples of 3 have already been described (p. 64).

$$11,111,111,111,111,111 = 2,071,723 \times 5,363,222,357$$
$$111,111,111,111,111,111 = 7 \times 9 \times 11 \times 13 \times 19$$
$$\times 37 \times 52,579 \times 333,667$$

No one has, however, as yet resolved the number obtained by writing 19 unit digits in a row.

We can synthesize a series of palindromes of unit digits by the following simple method:

$$1 \times 9 + 2 = 11$$
$$12 \times 9 + 3 = 111$$
$$123 \times 9 + 4 = 1111$$
$$1234 \times 9 + 5 = 11111$$

and so on until we reach

$$12345678 \times 9 + 9 = 111,111,111$$

This last expression is obviously equivalent to

$$12345679 \times 9 = 111,111,111$$

which contains no 8.

Suppose, now, we write the digits in ascending order, omitting 8, thus—

$$1 \quad 2 \quad 3 \quad 4 \quad 5 \quad 6 \quad 7 \quad 9$$

Select any digit, say 4, multiply it by 9, which gives us 36. Now multiply the whole expression by 36 and what do we get?

$$12345679 \times 36 = 444,444,444$$

If instead of 4 we had selected 7, we should obtain 63 on multiplying by 9, and

$$12345679 \times 63 = 777,777,777$$

Indeed, whatever digit we select, including even 8, it will appear nine times in succession in our final product.

This ceases to appear miraculous when we recall that

$$12345679 \times 9 = 111,111,111$$

for, to choose our first example,

$$
\begin{aligned}
12345679 \times 36 &= 12345679 \times 9 \times 4 \\
&= 111,111,111 \times 4 \\
&= 444,444,444
\end{aligned}
$$

Simple, isn't it? We recall Watson's remark in the story of "The Stockbroker's Clerk"—"Like all Holmes's reasoning the thing seemed simplicity itself when it was once explained."

$a^2 - b^2$

It is well known that if a and b represent two integers

$$a^2 - b^2 = (a + b)(a - b)$$

Suppose now we arbitrarily select any two numbers differing from each other by unity. Then $a - b = 1$ and

$$a^2 - b^2 = a + b$$

To begin with, let us put $a = 6$ and $b = 5$ then

$$a^2 - b^2 = 6 + 5 = 11$$

Putting $a = 56$ and $b = 45$,

$$(a^2 - b^2) = (a + b)(a - b) = 101 \times 11 = 1,111$$

Similarly if $a = 556$ and $b = 445$,

$$a^2 - b^2 = 1001 \times 111 = 111,111$$

In this way we can build up the following series—

$$
\begin{aligned}
6^2 - 5^2 &= 11 \\
56^2 - 45^2 &= 1111 \\
556^2 - 445^2 &= 111,111 \\
5556^2 - 4445^2 &= 11,111,111 \\
55556^2 - 44445^2 &= 1,111,111,111
\end{aligned}
$$

and so on.

If, now, we put $a = 7$ and $b = 4$ keeping as before $a + b = 11$, we find that

$$
\begin{aligned}
7 - 4 &= 3 \\
7^2 - 4^2 &= 33 \\
57^2 - 54^2 &= 333 \\
557^2 - 554^2 &= 3333 \\
5557^2 - 5554^2 &= 33333
\end{aligned}
$$

etc.

Putting $a = 8$ and $b = 3$

$$
\begin{aligned}
8 - 3 &= 5 \\
8^2 - 3^2 &= 55 \\
58^2 - 53^2 &= 555 \\
558^2 - 553^2 &= 5555
\end{aligned}
$$

etc.

Again, when $a = 9$ and $b = 2$

$$
\begin{aligned}
9 - 2 &= 7 \\
9^2 - 2^2 &= 77 \\
59^2 - 52^2 &= 777 \\
559^2 - 552^2 &= 7777
\end{aligned}
$$

etc.

Finally, when $a = 10$ and $b = 1$

$$10 - 1 = 9$$
$$10^2 - 1^2 = 99$$
$$60^2 - 51^2 = 999$$
$$560^2 - 551^2 = 9999$$
$$5560^2 - 5551^2 = 99999$$

etc.

Palindromes of 8 cannot be obtained in this way. A simple method is as follows:

$$9 \times 9 + 7 = 88$$
$$98 \times 9 + 6 = 888$$
$$987 \times 9 + 5 = 8888$$
$$9876 \times 9 + 4 = 88888$$

and so on until we come to

$$98765432 \times 9 + 0 = 888,888,888$$

Mention may here be made of yet another series of palindromes containing the digits 1 and 2.

$$11^2 - 0^2 = 121$$
$$61^2 - 50^2 = 1221$$
$$561^2 - 550^2 = 12221$$
$$5561^2 - 5550^2 = 122221$$

etc.

The Library Book

On turning over the title page of an ordinary printed book borrowed from the Public Library at Reading the other day, I noticed that its date in Hindu-Arabic numerals was not only palindromic but was unaltered by turning the paper upside down. Moreover, when placed in front of a mirror the reflection of the date was an exact replica of the date itself. Can you guess what the date was? (The answer is given on p. 189.)

IX

NUMBERS,

TRADITION AND SUPERSTITION

Pʀɪᴍɪᴛɪᴠᴇ man tends to be mystic. As knowledge has grown so has the belief in a connection between numbers and the occult. The idea has been so firmly rooted in us by countless generations of ancestors that even today most of us are unable to shake ourselves entirely free from the trammels of superstition and credulity. Who does not hesitate, for example, to walk under a ladder, to light three cigarettes with one and the same match, to sit thirteen at a table—to mention but a few of our peculiarities? Numerologists and students of Gematria in particular believe in the power of numbers and regard their lives as largely controlled by them. We are all conservative by nature, whatever our politics may be.

At a time when disease was regarded as the direct result of the Evil Eye it seemed reasonable to suppose that, if the latter could be neutralized, the ravages of disease would be checked automatically. As the Evil Eye could be controlled by spells, incantations and numbers, belief in a connection between numbers and health became firmly established. We shall come across numerous examples in the following pages.

Odd and Even Numbers

The distinction between odd and even numbers is, as perhaps we might expect, one of the earliest of arithmetical conceptions. In the Chinese Canon known as the "I-King" or "Book of Permutations," one of the most ancient of Chinese classics, believed to have been written around 1150 B.C., numbers are divided into two sets, namely the male or odd numbers and the female or even ones. Thus—

Male.............. 1   3   5   7   9   11 . . .
Female............   2   4   6   8   10   12 . . .

The complete sequence—

1   2   3   4   5   6   7   8 . . .

thus represents one female for each male, in other words, the perfect marriage.

Pythagoras, the famous Greek philosopher, who flourished some 550 B.C. and founded a school of mathematics at Crotona in Southern Italy, had travelled widely in his youth, and accepted these ideas. He brought them to Europe and added that he regarded even numbers as female because they were the more easy to deal with. Of course he was a bachelor at the time; it was not until later that he married Theono, one of his pupils. Even so his idea was probably true in those days when women had no legal status and must perforce do what they were told.

The game of "Odds and Evens" as played by

children dates back into dim antiquity; it was regarded as very old even in Plato's time, some 400 B.C. As usually played, one child holds in the closed hand a number of berries, pebbles, coins or other small objects and his playmates guess whether their number is odd or even.

The birth of a son was always regarded as an event of great happiness and importance to a family; a daughter was an unwanted, useless and expensive encumbrance. So odd numbers, which represented the male issue, symbolized good luck while the even ones brought poverty, sorrow and disaster. "The gods delight in odd numbers" wrote Virgil just before the beginning of the Christian Era, but even in his day that was already an ancient saw.

A practical application of this belief is versed by Samuel Lover (1839) in his "Rory O'More"—

"Now Rory, leave off Sir; you'll hug me no more,
  That's eight times today that you've kissed me before."
"Then here goes another" says he "to make sure,
"For there's luck in odd numbers" says Rory O'More.

Curiously enough in Palestinian folklore the exact opposite is maintained, every odd number, especially eleven, being regarded as unlucky. For this reason a one-eyed man is reputed to be difficult to get on with.

The humorist accuses the mathematician of insincerity in that one of his so-called odd digits finishes as even, namely seven! Let us now consider the digits individually.

ONE

For many centuries one was not regarded as a number but as the source of number, even as a brick is not a house, but bricks may be assembled to build a house. We are reminded of Michaelangelo's sage remark—

> Trifles make perfection and perfection is
> no trifle.

It was Stevin who, in 1585, pointed out that, if we take nothing from a given number, that number remains. If, however, we take any number whatever from a given number the latter does not remain intact. This is the case when we subtract one from any number; hence one must be a number. This sounds reasonably convincing.

Tradition says that the magpie was the only bird that refused to enter the Ark with Noah; in consequence it is unlucky to see one magpie. The ill-luck, however, is neutralized if the observer sees two of the birds and the effect becomes more involved as the number of magpies increases.

Thus in Lancashire, England, we are told that—

> "One is for anger, two for mirth,
>   Three for a wedding, four for a birth,
>   Five for rich, six for poor,
>   Seven for a witch; —I can tell you no more."

It has already been mentioned that in Palestine a one-eyed man is reputed to be difficult of approach. The fear that ill-luck will attend any who happen to meet such is emphasized in the "Arabian Nights' Entertainments" written at the close of the 15th century. The loquacious barber related to the Caliph the life histories of his six brothers—none of them very creditable. His fourth brother El-Kooz, who had lost his left eye, hearing that the King was about to go a-hunting, went to watch the procession. Unfortunately the King happened to see him and straightway cancelled the hunt, exclaiming "I seek refuge with God from the evil of this day." El-Kooz was severely beaten and left for dead, "For," said the King's attendant, "the King cannot endure the sight of a one-eyed person and especially when the defect is that of the left eye, for in this case he faileth not to put the person to death."

The Lutine Bell at Lloyds in London is struck once as a symbol of bad news. It was tolled once on Wednesday, February 6th, 1952, to announce the passing of George VI. Two strokes indicate good news.

On the other hand one could sometimes prove auspicious. Thus, for example, the horn of the unicorn possessed wonderful properties. It cured the plague and all manner of fevers; it would neutralize the poisons of mad dogs and venomous snakes. For these purposes it was used mainly in the form of a cordial.

The First of April is popularly known as "All Fools' Day" or, more correctly "Auld Fools' Day." In the Middle Ages the New Year began on March 25th. When this happened to fall during Passion

Week the New Year celebrations and presentations were usually postponed eight days, that is until April 1st. With the reform of the calendar by Pope Gregory XIII in 1582 it was ordained that the year should begin on the First day of January; the usual celebrations and exchange of presents therefore took place on that date, there being no religious tradition to cause postponement. Britain did not immediately adopt the Gregorian Calendar or New Style, as it was called. It was not until 1751 that Parliament ruled that the New Year of 1752 and all succeeding years should begin on January 1st. On April 1st mock presentations were frequently made with the charitable object of making fools of those who took them seriously, having perchance forgotten or overlooked the change of date.

Numerous proverbs emphasize the significance of the singular one or once. The ancient saws—

> Once is no custom,
> One swallow does not make a summer,

are familiar to all. None too complimentary are—

> Once a knave, always a knave,
> Once a man, twice a child.

A good piece of advice lies behind the adage—

> One good turn deserves another.

TWO

Two is unique in being the only even prime number. It plays an important part in ancient legends and mythology. Who has not heard of the Heavenly Twins, Castor and Pollux, heroes of the Battle of Lake Regillus, some 252 A.D., immortalized by Macaulay. Their stars shine in the heavens roughly halfway between Orion and the Great Bear. The Romans dedicated the second month of their year to Pluto, the god of Hades, and on the second day of that month they offered sacrifices to the Manes or Shades of the departed. The symbol of the Two-headed Eagle was first assumed by the Emperor Constantine (323–336 A.D.) to indicate his sovereignty over East and West.

Numerous proverbs embody the second digit. Thus—

> Two dogs over one bone seldom agree,

and the human parallel—

> Two of a trade seldom agree.

Others are—

> Two heads are better far than one, or why do folks marry?

> Two in distress make sorrow less,
> Two removals are as bad as a fire,

and

> He who follows two hares is sure to catch neither—

a Latin proverb, the English equivalent of which refers to having too many irons in the fire.

THREE

For millennia the third digit has been the object of superstition and even veneration. Possibly this dates back to the time when man could only count up to three and this number represented the upper limit of comprehension.

Three is called the "Mistress of Geometry" because a triangle has three sides and no area bounded by straight lines can have fewer. For the Greeks in particular the triangle possessed a special significance, and all through the ages it has played an important part in religious tradition and ritual. Thus, in the Trinity, we have the Early Christians' conception of three manifestations of one Deity—a sort of cushion between the polytheism of the Ancients and the strict monotheism of the Mohammedans in the one and only Allah. The word Trinity does not, of course, occur in Holy Writ; it is a later conception and was often represented by the devout as a triangle when they felt themselves unworthy to write the name of Deity. The supposed ill-luck attendant upon passing under a ladder is divine punishment for the sacrilege committed by the person who has the effrontery to break into the triangle made by the sloping ladder. The veneration of the triple-leaved clover and shamrock (p. 123), as also of the triple crown of the Pope's Tiara, is similarly connected with the Trinity.

On his third voyage from Europe into the unknown west in 1498, Columbus saw three mountain peaks slowly rise above the horizon. On approaching more closely he found that they were part of one and the same mountain on a single island. Recognizing this as a symbol of the Trinity, he named the island Trinidad.

Of all regular plane figures the equilateral triangle possesses the sharpest angles; it was therefore used by medieval alchemists as the symbol for fire. It was well known that most things are decomposed by heat and it was assumed that the fire, with its sharp angles, poked its way in between the particles of compact substances and thus effected their decomposition. Sulphur or brimstone—that is, the burning stone—was regarded as the essence of combustibility because it readily burns away completely, leaving virtually no ash. It was therefore represented by a triangle with a cross beneath, thus $\triangle\!\!\!+$. The cross appears in many medieval symbols and represents the close connection believed to exist between religion and alchemy.

The words three and thrice occur many times in both the Old and the New Testaments. Three men visited Abraham as he sat by his tent on the plains of Mamre during the heat of the day (*Genesis* 18); three times Balaam's ass refused to proceed on its journey and was three times smitten for its disobedience (*Numbers* 22). Three days after Joseph had interpreted their dreams, Pharaoh's butler and baker were released from prison, the former to be restored to favor, the latter to be hanged (*Genesis* 40). The plague of darkness covered the Land of Egypt for three days; the people "saw not one another, neither rose any from his place for three days" (*Exodus* 10). Jonah was imprisoned in the body of the whale for three days and three nights. There were three Cities of Refuge on each side of the Jordan to which alleged criminals might fly for sanctuary.

Again, in the New Testament we read "For as Jonas was three days and three nights in the whale's belly, so shall the Son of Man be three days and three nights in the heart of the earth." (*Matthew* 12). For three days Saul was without sight (*Acts* 9). At the Last Supper Christ turned to Peter saying "Before the cock crow twice, thou shalt deny me thrice" (*Mark* 14), and so it turned out to be.

In medieval trials by the ordeal of hot iron the defendant seized a bar of iron that had been heated in a fire during a ceremonial service, and walked three paces with it before letting it fall. He then proceeded to the altar where the officiating priest bandaged the wound. In three days' time he again appeared before the priest whose duty it was to state whether or not the wound had healed. If it had healed in so short a time it was clearly a miracle; deity had intervened to prove the man's innocence. But we can see loopholes.

Three instruments were used by the Roman Catholic Church when pronouncing excommunication, namely the Bell, the Book and the Candle. The custom is ancient and possibly dates back to the 8th century. The bell was tinkled to apprise all present; the sentence was read by the officiating

bishop out of a book which symbolized the authority
of the Church; finally the bishop and his twelve
priests, each of whom carried a lighted candle,
dashed them on to the ground and extinguished the
flames. Although this last act symbolized the
spiritual darkness of the excommunicatee, it also
gave hope in that, as the candles could be relighted
so the ban might be lifted upon repentance.

According to legend St. Nicholas of Myra, in the
4th century, gave three bags of gold, one each, to the
three unmarried daughters of a poor but worthy
merchant. He thus enabled them to marry, a procedure that at the time was impossible without a
suitable dowry.

Gold, frankincense and myrrh are offered annually
on the Sovereign's behalf at the annual Epiphany
Service in the Queen's Chapel in the grounds of
Marlborough House, London. The custom is sym-
bolic of the offerings made by the Three Wise Men
or Magi to the infant Jesus and has been observed
over some 800 years. The legend of the Magi, who
have been described as three Eastern monarchs
guided by a star to Bethlehem to see the Christ in
His manger, is perpetuated today in the sign of the
Three Crowns at many English inns. The one at
Lichfield is famous, adjoining as it does the house
where Dr. Johnson was born in 1709. Lichfield is
famous also in having a cathedral with three spires—
the only one in Great Britain.

In the Tragedy of Macbeth Shakespeare empha-
sizes the importance of three in witchcraft.

> "When shall we three meet again,
> In thunder, lightning, or in rain?"

asks one of the three foul, bearded witches of her
wild and withered companions. In due course the
trio did meet again hand in hand on a desolate heath
during a thunderstorm chanting—

> "Thrice to thine and thrice to mine
> And thrice again, to make up nine.
> Peace! The charm's wound up."

Yet again, somewhat later, the same three witches
appear in a dark cave, in the middle of which a
cauldron is on the boil, preparing its hell broth.
"Thrice," says the first, "the brinded cat hath
mewed." "Thrice," repeats the second. "'Tis time,
'tis time," reiterates the third.

In (I *Kings* 17) we read that Elijah lodged for
some time in the house of a widow at Zarephath, the
modern Sarafand roughly midway between Tyre
and Sidon. During his stay the widow's son was taken
ill and "died." The prophet carried the lad upstairs,
laid him upon his own bed and stretched himself
upon the child three times. After the third attempt
"the soul of the child came into him again and he
revived." It was the three that did it. Today our
Press would content themselves with prosaically
reporting that methods of artificial respiration were
applied and the child made a prompt recovery.

The trefoil or Herb Trinity was traditionally the
plant used by St. Patrick to illustrate the mystery
of the Trinity (p. 118); it was one of the many species

of triple-leaved plants adopted by the Irish as their Emblem under the general name of seamrog or shamrock. By virtue of their triple nature the trefoils were noisome to witches and effective against their spells. The ancient druids held the clover in high esteem for this reason. Pliny in his *Natural History* written at the beginning of the Christian Era remarks (Book XXI, Chapter 88) that the trefoil is a particularly good remedy for the stings of scorpions and serpents, the seeds being taken in wine. A wash prepared from the seeds of the trefoil is described as "extremely beneficial for preserving the freshness of the skin in females." At times when people seldom washed, as for example in the Middle Ages, we can well believe this to have been true. The clover, by the way, is the "Clubs" of the pack of cards; indeed the word clover is derived from the same root as club.

Pliny says that some persons were wont to mix water in equal proportions from three different wells and, after making a libation with part of it in a new earthen vessel, they administered the residue to patients suffering from tertian fever. As a cure for boils Pliny mentions the practice of wetting them three times with fasting saliva. Spitting three times on the ground when medicine is taken was supposed to help the good work. Upon the appearance of a stranger or when a person looked at a sleeping infant, the faithful nurse would spit three times upon the ground; this prevented any harm from coming to the child.

Three in the morning is a traditionally critical time for people sick unto death. In medieval times, three scruples of the ashes of a witch, who had been roasted at the stake, were a sure protection against witchcraft—and a guarantee of good health.

The early conception of three as the upper limit of counting led to its use in an indefinite sense to indicate a relatively large number. Thus it frequently happens that the Greek *tri* and the English thrice are used in this way. For example, Hermes, supposed inventor of numbers, mathematics and astronomy, was styled *trismegistos*, literally thrice greatest. Hermes was the son of Zeus, born of a morning, by midday he had invented the lyre; at eve he stole 50 head of cattle from Apollo, which he hid so skillfully in a cave that they could not be found. He then returned to his cot and lay down quietly as a baby should. Small wonder that he was termed thrice greatest, suggesting a greatness beyond compare.

A similar idea lies behind the use of thrice in several of Shakespeare's plays. Thus Henry VI says—

> "What stronger breastplate than a heart untainted!
> Thrice is he arm'd that hath his quarrel just."

Some may prefer Artemus Ward's rendering—

> "Thrice is he arm'd that hath his quarrel just,
> And four times he who gets his fist in fust."

In Milton's "Thrice Happy Isles," Tennyson's

"Thrice blest whose lives are faithful prayers" and Allan Ramsay's "Thrice happy life that's from ambition free," the indefinite magnitude is clearly intended.

Many people shrink from lighting three cigarettes from one match, and it has long been imagined that if an accident occurs two more will happen in a very short time. Women who have broken a valuable vase or ornament will sometimes smash two other objects of negligible value to break the run of ill-luck.

The three-legged mare is an early nickname for the gallows. We give three cheers to welcome the favorite, while to him who has failed we repeat the slogan of William Edward Hickson—

Try, try, try again.

Indeed, whichever way we turn we find a traditional three forcing its attention upon us. Even the cook allots a classical three minutes for the boiling of an egg, and Jerome K. Jerome writes of "Three Men in a Boat."

"Number three is always fortunate" wrote Tobias Smollett in *Peregrine Pickle* in 1751. It was a number to conjure with.

As already mentioned, odd numbers have long been regarded in Europe as lucky. Three has usually been associated with specially good luck, probably for a variety of reasons. An added significance lay in its being the first odd number at a time when one was not regarded as a number but a builder of numbers.

There would, however, appear to be a limit to this good luck if the Scottish proverb is true—

All things thrive but thrice.

FOUR

Four is our first square and as such symbolizes that which is fair and just. Thus, for example, a hungry man relishes a good square meal, the honest trader a good square deal, and most of us prefer things on the square. It is possibly for this reason that so many of the ancient fonts in our churches have four-sided bowls, for the church represents that which is fair, just, honorable and of good repute. I have never seen a three-sided font suggestive of the Trinity.

The Greeks thought highly of the number. Hermes was born in the fourth month of the year and Athenians honored him with sacrifices on the fourth day of every month. Aristotle (384–322 B.C.) pupil of Plato and tutor to Alexander the Great, postulated the existence of four elements, Fire, Air, Earth and Water. Recognition of the four seasons of the year dates back far into antiquity.

The name for deity in most ancient religions comprised four letters. Thus

Assyrian	*Adad*	German	*Gott*
Egyptian	*Amen*	French	*Dieu*
Persian	*Sire*	Turk	*Esar*
Greek	*Theos*	Tartar	*Itgu*
Latin	*Deus*	Arabic	*All'h*

The finding of freak specimens of four-leaved clover, in which the leaflets are arranged in the form of a cross, is good luck. The leaves were formerly held to be specially sacred, enabling the bearer to detect the Evil Eye and thus escape from its baneful influence. They were a sure cure for diseases both mental and physical.

Flowers with four petals arranged cross-wise, known to the botanist as crucifers or cross bearers, were likewise regarded as beneficent. Many such have been pressed into the service of man; some for food, such as watercress, cabbage and cauliflower; others for condiments and medicines, to wit the horse-radish, mustard, and a host of others. The Greeks had a proverb advising men to—

Eat cress to learn more wit.

FIVE

Five was the group number used by many early peoples, no doubt because the normal hand has five fingers, including the thumb (p. 14). A bunch of fives is a slang term for the fist.

The Jews were wont to divide a bride's attendants into groups of five; this is illustrated in Christ's parable of the virgins, five of whom were wise and five otherwise (*Matthew* 25). Among the Romans it was customary to burn five wax candles at a marriage ceremony and to offer special prayers to five deities.

Man is endowed with five senses. The body of Christ on the Cross bore five wounds and charms chanted five times together with five paternosters were employed in medieval times to staunch the flow of blood.

The Wizard's Pentagram

This was the Pythagorean symbol for health and comprised three large triangles so arranged as to yield a central pentagon, on each side of which rests a triangle (Fig. 19). It may also be regarded as five A's arranged symmetrically to yield a five-rayed

Figure 19. THE WIZARD'S FOOT, PENTAGRAM OR PENTALPHA

star, whence the name pentalpha. The design can be drawn complete without raising pen from paper— an excellent example of Euler's Rule.

Its connection with the triangles rather than with the five wounds of Christ gave it mystic powers acknowledged by Hindus, Mohammedans and Cabalists alike. It was used as a talisman against misfortune, being carved on babies' cots, chalked on doorsteps and lintels, to ward off the Evil Eye. Thus the Devil, in the guise of Goethe's Mephistopheles, says—

"My steps by one slight obstacle controlled—
The Wizard's Foot that on your threshold is."

Five, like three, has frequently been used in the indefinite sense equivalent to "a few" or "some." Thus we read in the Old Testament (*Genesis* 43) that the sons of Jacob brought their youngest brother Benjamin to see Joseph in Egypt. When they sat at a meal together it was noticed that "Benjamin's mess was five times" as much as that of any of his brothers. In modern parlance Benjamin received the lion's share.

In the romantic legend of the duel between Goliath and David, related in true Homeric style in I *Samuel* 17, we read that David "chose him five smooth stones out of the brook" and with sling in hand bravely set out to meet his gigantic opponent. Here again five is the group number, equivalent to several.

SIX

Six has been designated the human number for in one of the accounts of creation as outlined in Genesis we are told that man was created on the sixth day. It was moreover laid down that man, like his Creator, should work for six days out of every seven (*Exodus* 20, 9), an injunction that many are today trying to avoid.

Six is one less than seven, the symbol of completion and perfection, but man may take comfort in the fact that six is mathematically perfect; that is to say, its divisors 1, 2 and 3 add up to its own value of 6, as has already been mentioned (p. 41).

The ancient druids had a special reverence for six; they went six together in great ceremony on the sixth day of the moon to cut the mistletoe.

The mystic Seal of Solomon comprises two equilateral triangles set crosswise as shown in Fig. 20. The central hexagon is surrounded by six small equilateral triangles, and the seal may therefore be regarded as six A's symmetrically disposed round each other—whence the name hexalpha. It possessed similar powers to the pentalpha in that it warded off the Evil Eye, thereby protecting the wearer from misfortune and disease.

Figure 20. SOLOMON'S SEAL OR THE HEXALPHA

Miscellanea

To be at sixes and sevens is to be in disorder. In the days when candles were popular, long sixes were those weighing six to the pound and measuring some eight inches in length; short sixes were only about four inches long. Six is the maximum number of dots on the face of a die or, usually, in the compartment of a domino. (Some sets of dominoes go up to nine.) Six is also the bee's number. Who taught the bee that for a comb to hold the maximum amount of honey with the minimum amount of wax in a framework of maximum strength, the structure should be hexagonal? The bees solved that problem ages before man appeared on the earth even as the spider learned to produce geometrical patterns with its silken thread.

SEVEN

Seven appears to have been regarded from time immemorial as possessing a special mystical significance. It represents completion and spiritual perfection. Possibly this is in some way connected with its being the sum of three and four, the former representing good luck and the latter justice.

The seven wonders of the world were the Pyramids of Egypt; the Hanging (or terraced) Gardens of Babylon; the Temple of Diana at Ephesus; the Statue of Jupiter by Phideas at Athens; the Colossus at Rhodes, an image in brass of the Sun God Apollo; the Mausoleum at Halicarnassus, the tomb of Mausolus, King of Caria, erected by his queen Artemisia; finally the Pharos at Alexandria, built of white marble by Ptolemy. The palace of Cyrus is sometimes substituted for the last named.

Ancient Rome was the City of Seven Hills—the Capitoline, the most important historically, the Aventine, Palatine, Quirinal, Viminal, Esquiline and Caelius.

The seven wise men distinguished in antiquity included Thales of Miletus, 640–550 B.C.; Solon of

Athens, 640–559 B.C. There was less agreement on the other five.

A horseshoe, symbol of good luck, has holes for seven nails. An old horseshoe fastened on the stable door kept the witches away; but the horseshoe nailed to the mast of the *Victory* did not save Nelson at Trafalgar in 1805; it was upside down and the luck ran out! Or was it satisfied with giving Nelson the victory?

Seven has long been regarded as associated with healing virtues. In the Old Testament, for example, we are told the story of Naaman the Syrian who was also a leper. His king Jehoram sent him to Elisha to be cured (II *Kings* 5). The prophet told him, "Go, wash in the Jordan seven times and thy flesh shall come again to thee and thy flesh shall be clean." Naaman grumbled a bit, but eventually did as he was bid and when he emerged from the river for the seventh time "his flesh came again like unto the flesh of a little child."

Elisha's healing power is linked with seven in yet another story, that of the child of the woman at Shunem who had offered the prophet hospitality. The boy accompanied his father into the fields and apparently suffered from a sunstroke. He was taken home and "died." The distressed mother sought Elisha who was at Carmel and implored his help. The prophet returned to the house and stretched himself upon the child. "The child sneezed seven times" and opened his eyes (II *Kings* 4).

Years ago country folk believed that the seventh

son in a family possessed unusual gifts and if he happened to be the seventh son of a seventh son he was indeed a prodigy. In his hands, for example, the divining rod used for detecting underground water was particularly effective. Numerous tales are on record of sick persons who have been cured through the good offices of seventh sons. A seventh daughter was blessed with similar powers.

It has been pointed out that man has seven parts, namely head, chest, abdomen and four limbs. Again, man has seven organs including the heart, liver, lungs, stomach, spleen and two kidneys. Finally his head has seven connections with world around him; these are through the eyes, ears, mouth and two nostrils. It is said that seven stages of drunkenness may be discerned, namely the irritable, mellow, pugnacious, affectionate, lachrymose, followed by collapse and death.

Shakespeare refers to the seven ages of man—but these are not all to his credit. "Seven heads of fat bats" were prescribed for internal ailments by John Gadsden, physician to Edward III.

Seven pure colors are recognized in the spectrum, namely red, orange, yellow, green, blue, indigo and violet. These, in sunlight, are blended together to form white light, as first shown by Sir Isaac Newton in 1666.

In 1781 Sir William Herschel made astronomical history by the discovery of a seventh planet whilst studying the sky in the neighborhood of Castor and Pollux. The ancients had long known six planets, namely Mercury, Venus, the Earth, Mars, Jupiter and Saturn; here was the seventh, completing the holy number; the tale was thus complete. In accordance with custom the planet was christened after a heathen deity, Uranus. Eight years later Klaproth discovered a new metal in a black mineral then believed to be an ore of iron. In compliment to the British astronomer he named the metal uranium. More than a century elapsed before anyone realized what an important part uranium might play in war and peace alike.

Although Uranus is the seventh and outermost planet visible to the unaided eye, two others are known, namely Neptune, discovered in 1846 and Pluto in 1930, the latter named after the god of the underworld. Are there any more?

Seven is the maximum number of eclipses of the sun and moon that can occur in any one year. Usually there are fewer; the minimum number is two, in which case both are eclipses of the sun. In 1935 there were seven, five of the sun and two of the moon.

The well-known constellations of the Great Bear or Charles' Wain and the Little Bear each contain seven prominent stars. Julius Caesar referred to the former as *Septemtriones*, the Seven Oxen. The tip of the tail of the Little Bear is Polaris, the Pole Star. Legend has it that the giant Atlas was expelled by the gods from Olympus and condemned to hold the Heavens and the Earth on his shoulders. Pleone was his wife and they had seven daughters who appear in the heavens as the Pleiades.

It is not surprising that seven should figure prominently in early religious beliefs. According to the Old Testament legend of the Creation, God completed his work in six days—a mathematically perfect number—and rested upon the seventh day. The Jews therefore hold the seventh day as particularly holy, calling it the Sabbath, a Hebrew word that appears to be connected with the Arabic *sebà* seven. The Babylonian seventh day, on the other hand, was unlucky. The early Christians broke away from tradition, choosing Sunday, the first day of the week, as their day of rest.

According to one account of the Deluge as given in *Genesis* 7, Noah had seven days' warning of the catastrophe. He was instructed to take seven pairs of every clean beast and of every fowl of the air into the Ark. After the waters had subsided Noah liberated, at intervals of seven days, a dove for purposes of reconnaissance. In the seventh month the Ark rested on Mt. Ararat after a phenomenal voyage.

Jacob, we are told in *Genesis* 29, served Laban seven years for his daughter Leah and yet another seven for Rachel. An echo of this is to be found in the old-time apprenticeship of seven years. We are all familiar with the legend of the Pharaoh who dreamed of the seven well-favored kine that were followed and eaten by seven lean kine. He also dreamed that seven ears of good corn were devoured by a like number of thin ears, blasted with the east wind. These dreams were interpreted by Joseph as indicating that Egypt would be blest with seven years of plenty, to be followed by seven years of famine (*Genesis* 41).

The fall of Jericho was intimately associated with seven. Once each day for six days a procession marched round the city. The procession comprised armed men accompanied by seven priests with seven trumpets. On the seventh day the city was perambulated seven times and on the seventh round when the priests blew their trumpets, the walls most conveniently fell flat (*Joshua* 6).

The Feast of Tabernacles, an echo of which is found in the Harvest Festivals of the Christian churches, was held in the autumn to mark the close of the harvest. It took place in the seventh month *Tishri* of the Jewish Ecclesiastical year and lasted seven days, during which the people were enjoined to make merry (*Deut.* 16).

The seven champions of Christendom were St. George for merry England, St. Andrew for Scotland, St. Patrick for Ireland, St. David for Wales, St. Denis for France, St. James for Spain and St. Anthony for Italy.

The seven deadly sins are given as pride, avarice, lust, anger, gluttony, envy and sloth, while the seven gifts of the Holy Ghost are wisdom, counsel, fortitude, godliness, knowledge, understanding and fear of the Lord. In the New Testament James (3, 17) gives the seven characters of wisdom. The seven sleepers were seven Christian youths at Ephesus, who under the persecution of Decius sheltered in a cave *circa* 250 A.D. Their pursuers walled them up, and tradition says they fell into a deep sleep, like Rip Van Winkle, awaking a couple of centuries later.

Cabalists postulate the existence of seven heavens of increasing happiness as one passes from the first or lowest upwards to the seventh, which is the abode of God himself. A person in the seventh heaven is thus in a most exalted state of happiness.

The Mau Mau regard seven with special reverence; it plays an important part in their initiation ritual.

Miscellanea

The legend of Robert Bruce and the Spider is a familiar one. Bruce was crowned at Scone in 1305, but fled before the English and hid on Rathlin Island. In a cave he one day watched a spider make six unsuccessful attempts to affix its web to the roof. "Will the silly creature try again?" asked Bruce of himself. The silly creature did try yet again and—succeeded. A ray of hope pierced the darkness. Six times had Bruce tried to oust the English and six times had he failed. Like the spider he would try once more. He did. He left the Isle in 1307 and within two years was in control of nearly the whole of Scotland. Seven had brought him success.

Who is not familiar with the old nursery query—

> As I was going to St. Ives
> I met a man with seven wives;
> Each wife had seven sacks,
> Each sack had seven cats,
> Each cat had seven kits.
> How many kits, cats, sacks and wives
> Were there going to St. Ives?

When casting lots for games children often use the rhyme—

> One, two, three, four, five, six, seven,
> All good children go to heaven.

and so on.

The *indefinite* seven occurs in many expressions such as (*Proverbs* 26, 16)—

> "The sluggard is wiser in his own conceit
> than seven men."

And again—

> One lie needs seven lies to wait upon it.

EIGHT

As seven represents completion, eight suggests a fresh start. For this reason many ancient fonts in our churches are octagonal, representing the new life which the child enters on baptism. The Devil escaped through the north door, specially opened for the purpose, as the water was poured on the child and the infant became cleansed in both body and mind.

Eight is the first cube and thus introduces the third dimension.

In the Scriptures we find repeated reference to eight. Thus Noah was the eighth person to be saved in the Ark (II *Peter*, 2, 5); circumcision took place on the eighth day (*Genesis* 17, 12); Christ himself rose on the first day of the week, that is the eighth day, one over the seven. Christ enunciated eight beati-

tudes to his disciples (*Matthew* 5) and these are regarded as an analysis of perfect spiritual well being.

The Greeks regarded eight as an all powerful
number; they had a proverb—

All things are eight.

NINE

Nine is the first odd square; it is one more than
eight and the expression "one over the eight" has
a well-known, humorously sinister meaning. As three
represents the Trinity, three times three is called
the perfect plural and nine becomes mystic.

Nine has also been regarded as the emblem of
matter. As matter is indestructible so is nine, for if
we multiply any number whatever by nine the sum
of the digits of the product is always nine or a
multiple of nine, as we have already seen.

The Greeks believed that nine rivers flowed into
Hades; they also postulated the existence of nine
muses, daughters of Zeus, referred to in poetry as
"The Nine." Macaulay began his immortal poem
to Horatius by referring to the nine Etruscan gods—

Lars Porsena of Clusium,
By the nine gods he swore . . .

The Sabines also had nine gods—the Novosiles.

An ancient measure of length is the span, nomin-
ally the distance a man's hand could stretch, but
later accepted as equivalent to nine inches. The
indefinite span occurs in such expression as "Our
life is but a span."

A cat possesses remarkable muscular vitality and is said to have nine lives. "Nine days wonder" refers to something that causes a great sensation and then is quickly forgotten. The old proverb, alluding to the fact that puppies, as well as kittens, are born blind—"a wonder lasts nine days and then the puppy's eyes are open"—doubtless infers that the public is blind with astonishment for nine days and then sees clearly and ceases to wonder. In Cornwall the irritations on children's eyes, known locally as whilks, were cured by passing the tail of a black cat nine times over the affected places. Nine is thus the feline number, just as six is the human. To look nine ways is to squint, but for that unfortunate malady there does not appear to be an equally simple cure.

The whip used for legal corporal punishment was known as the cat o'nine tails or nine tail bruiser.

Human blood is red, so a red color symbolizes good health. A red thread or cord worn round the neck is a sure preventive of nose bleeding, provided always that it is tied in front in nine knots. Nine successive days' rubbing with the inside of a broad bean pod will cure warts.

The game of ninepins is a form of skittles in which nine "pins" are set upright to be knocked down by a ball. In the expression "right as ninepence" the ninepence is a corruption of nine pins, whereas a "nimble ninepence" is quite different. It refers to the silver ninepenny coin in common use until 1696;* it was soft and easily bent or "nimble." When bent

* The Irish shilling was known as ninepence.

it was used as a love token, whence the old adage—

> A nimble ninepence is better than a slow
> shilling.

For several centuries the Nine of Diamonds has been called the "Curse of Scotland" and although at least a dozen explanations of the reason for this have been proposed the true one still seems to be in doubt.

The *indefinite* nine occurs in a number of expressions such as—

> Possession is nine points of the law.
> Nine times out of ten.
> A stitch in time saves nine.

An old saw states that—

> Nine tailors make a man.

It is now an expression of contempt for the poor physique of tailors; but that was not the original idea. Tailor is a corruption of teller, the number of strokes on the funeral bell; three for children, six for women and nine for men.

A Latin proverb makes the invidious distinction that while—

> Seven is a banquet, nine is a brawl.

When an article fits "to the nines" it is a perfect fit.

TEN

The word ten appears to have been derived from a compound word meaning two hands. In the ancient Teutonic language known as Gothic, the numeral was known as taihun or taihund. In our word ten the Gothic *h* has disappeared (p. 15).

Ancient Rome had her ten Tribunes elected to protect the plebeians from any patrician injustice. The Decemviri or Ten Men were a commission of ten appointed some 450 B.C. to collect and publish the legal customs of the State.

Ten, like three, five and several other numbers, is frequently used in an *indefinite* sense. Thus the more influential persons in a community are styled the Upper Ten. When Hannah mourned that she had no children, her husband Elkanah asked "Why weepest thou? . . . am not I better to thee than ten sons?" (I *Samuel* 1, 8). When Nehemiah returned to Jerusalem from exile in the 5th century B.C. the Jews are said to have warned him ten times of dangers ahead (*Nehemiah* 4, 12).

The first ten days of Tishri—the seventh month of the Jewish Ecclesiastical Year—are called the Ten Days of Penitence and are spent by orthodox Jews in meditation and solemn preparation for the Day of Atonement, that is the tenth day, the most solemn in the year. The tenth day of the tenth month, Tivise, is observed as a fast in remembrance of the siege of Jerusalem by Nebuchadnezzar which tradition says was begun on this day.

The ancient Hebrews had graduated systems for wet and dry measures which were partly decimal. For example, 10 acres of vineyard yielded one bath—a liquid measure approximating to 70 pints. The ephah was laid down as the tenth part of the homer (*Ezekiel* 45, 11)—a dry measure, approximating to our bushel. To this extent they were ahead of us who even in this enlightened age keep to the clumsy measures of our fathers, such as 4 quarts to the gallon and 8 bushels to the quarter.

The payment of tithe, the tenth part, is ancient practice. Abraham, some 2100 B.C., paid tithe to Melchizedek, King of Salem; Jacob some years later vowed at Bethel to return to God one tenth of all that he received.

When God decided to destroy Sodom because of its wickedness Abraham extracted a promise that the city should be saved if as few as ten righteous could be found therein. Alas, the city was destroyed.

The Commandments engraved on two tablets of stone numbered ten and are in consequence known as the Decalogue.

In *Psalm* 33 the righteous are enjoined to—

"Praise the Lord with harp: Sing unto Him with the psaltery and an instrument of ten strings."

The lyre, be it noted, had only seven strings. Numerous other references to ten occur in both the Old and the New Testaments. In the latter the Kingdom of Heaven is likened unto ten virgins (p. 127); ten lepers met Christ as he entered a village (*Luke* 17, 12); the nobleman about to leave for a far country called his ten servants and delivered unto them ten pounds (*Luke* 19, 13).

And so we might go on.

ELEVEN

Being an odd number eleven is not usually regarded in Europe as being associated with ill luck, but rather the reverse.

According to Palestinian folklore, however, eleven is distinctly unlucky. Whether or not this is associated with the tradition that malaria, that scourge of the Middle East, often proved fatal on the eleventh day, is not known. Alexander the Great died in his prime at 32, B.C. 323, on the eleventh day and so did Byron in 1824, again on the eleventh day after the initial attack of that disease. A few such cases and the baneful superstition would quickly be established.

The scriptures are satisfied with ten commandments, but human frailty has introduced an eleventh, namely—

Thou shalt not be found out.

The ancient Spartans a couple of millennia ago apparently subscribed to this view, but will the clergy of today?

TWELVE

The earliest code of Roman law compiled by the Decemviri was engraved on twelve bronze tablets—the "Twelve Tables." A jury comprises twelve persons who decide whether or not the charges brought against the defendant are true.

To talk nineteen to the dozen indicates extremely rapid speech. The baker's dozen (p. 147), the long dozen and the Devil's dozen mean thirteen. To give a person a baker's dozen is slang for a good hiding—all the recipient deserves and one over. The indefinite dozen occurs in "a dozen times." Byron spoke of "a round dozen of authors" and others.

The Twelfth Night is that of 5th January, the eve of the twelfth day after Christmas. It was a time for great merrymaking, commemorating the manifestation of Christ to the Magi. Possibly it was a survival of the old Roman Saturnalia and Shakespeare's play produced in 1602 was so named because it was specially written for Twelfth Night Festivities.

In the Middle Ages it was a common saying that every English archer carried "twelve Scotsmen under his girdle." The archers were renowned for the accuracy of their aim and each carried twelve arrows in his belt. That the above saying was not a mere empty English boast would appear from the words of Froissart, the famous French historian, who wrote at the close of the 14th century—"Of a truth the Scottish cannot boast great skill with the bow, but rather bear axes with which, in time of need, they give heavy strokes."

An old Gloucestershire saw runs "It aint spring until you can plant your foot upon twelve daisies."

The belt in the heavens through which the sun appeared to travel, known as the Zodiac, was in ancient times divided into twelve sections each containing a group of prominent stars, constellations or signs. Much as we today, musing by a fire of red hot cinders, imagine grotesque figures to be depicted therein, so the ancients conceived of the constellations as outlining various animals and men. They came to be known as the signs of the Zodiac, the last word derived from the Greek *zōon* animal. The signs are believed to have originated in Mesopotamia, for the animals are Biblical. There is no mention, for example, of the alligator or hippopotamus, which were well known in Egypt, but not in Palestine or Arabia. The signs are usually expressed as follows:

The Ram, the Bull, the Heavenly Twins,
And next the Crab the Lion Shines,
The Virgin and the Scales.
The Scorpion, Archer and He-goat,
The Man that holds the watering pot
And Fish with shining tails.

The twelve sons of Jacob gave rise to the twelve tribes of Israel and an echo of this occurs in the twelve disciples chosen by Christ.

Twelve was associated with all kinds of Hebrew ritual. When the Jordan was crossed Joshua set up twelve stones in the midst of the river as a memorial (*Joshua* 4, 9). The round bronze tank made by Solomon stood upon twelve oxen (I *Kings* 7, 25). Elijah erected on Mt. Carmel an altar out of twelve stones (I *Kings* 18, 31); later he found Elisha, who was destined to be his successor, ploughing with twelve yoke of oxen (I *Kings* 19, 19). Twelve he-goats were sacrificed as a sin offering (*Ezra*, 6, 17). At the age of twelve Christ was found by his parents in the temple (*Luke* 2, 42).

THIRTEEN

Among Western Europeans thirteen is universally regarded with disfavor, although it is stated that in Southern Italy the reverse is the case. It is an old superstition usually attributed to the events of the Last Supper when Christ sat at meal with the Twelve (*Mark* 14). Judas is reputed to have been the first to leave and shortly afterwards, filled with remorse at betraying his Master, he went out and hanged himself.

But probably the superstition is much older than that; it could easily have arisen in a variety of ways. Thus, for example, while twelve is readily divisible by several digits, thirteen is prime with no divisors other than one and itself. It is thus a most awkward number to deal with. Other possible explanations will readily suggest themselves to the reader.

But whatever the cause, the fact remains, so much so that many hotels number their thirteenth rooms 12A or 14, as they find guests often hesitate to accept one marked 13. The forces of evil are too stupid to realize that room 12A or 14 may still be the thirteenth. Henry Ford, who built up a huge industry, could not be induced to undertake any serious business on Friday the thirteenth of any month.

The origin of thirteen to the baker's dozen has nothing whatever to do with superstition. When, years ago, anyone selling bread in short weight was liable to extremely harsh penalties, the London bakers sought to escape these by adding an extra loaf, known as the "in bread" or "vantage loaf" to each dozen sold.

A thirteener was a silver shilling formerly current in Ireland worth 13 pence in Irish copper currency.

In the middle ages thirteen pence halfpenny is alleged to have been the remuneration for a hangman, and a piece of money of this value appears to have been in use in the reign of James I of Scotland (1424 to 1437).

FORTY

This has been and still is frequently used as a round number. Thus "forty winks" means a short nap.

We are all familiar with "Ali Baba and his forty thieves"—probably again a round number. At one time 40 pence were customary in wagers. Quarantine, as the word implies, referred to a period of forty days during which persons who might spread a contagious or infectious disease were isolated from the rest of the community. Gradually, however, the idea of forty days was discarded and quarantine came to mean, as it does today, the act of isolation rather than the time itself spent in isolation.

In both the Old and the New Testaments we find the indefinite forty. Moses, addressing the Children of Israel, repeated the words that God had said to him—

> "These forty years the Lord thy God hath been with thee." (*Deuteronomy* 2, 7)

In *Joshua* 5, 6 we read that "The Children of Israel walked forty years in the Wilderness." Christ was in the wilderness for forty days (*Mark* 1, 13) and after the resurrection was seen by the apostles for a like forty days (*Acts* 1, 3).

SEVENTY

Like forty, seventy has been frequently used in the indefinite sense. Macaulay tells us that Aulus, who fought heroically at the Battle of Lake Regillus *c.* 252 A.D., was a "man of seventy fights." In the New Testament seventy times seven is used as an indefinitely large number (*Matthew* 18).

THOUSAND

This was the largest number in common use by the Romans to be represented by a single letter, namely M, the initial letter of *mille*, the Latin word for one thousand. For many centuries it has been largely used also in the indefinite sense to indicate a large number. This is embodied in the well-known expression "I have a thousand and one things to do."

In the Old Testament we are told (I *Samuel* 18, 7) that Saul became outrageously jealous of David because, after the slaying of Goliath, women sang "Saul has slain his thousands but David his ten thousands." In the Book of the Revelation we read that the number of angels round the throne was "ten thousand times ten thousand," that is, infinitely large.

MILLION

The word million, is derived from the Latin *mille*, coupled with the augmentative suffix *on;* it thus means a great thousand just as balloon is big ball and saloon is big salle or hall. It was apparently first used by the Italian mathematician Planudes *c.* 1340. One of its earliest appearances in English occurs in Langland's "Piers the Plowman" of the same century. It is here enjoined—

> Coveyte (covet) not his goodes
> For milions of money.

Like thousand, million is often used to indicate an indefinitely large number. Although we talk glibly of millions we cannot really appreciate what a million means. Even the Bible does not contain a million words, only 774,746. A million men placed shoulder to shoulder would give a line approximately 160 miles in length.

BILLION

For this word we appear to be indebted to the French. Chuquet used it in 1484 to denote 10^{12}. This is its correct use for it is derived from the Latin *bis* twice and million, suggesting two millions multiplied together. The French later used it as an alternative to milliard or 10^9 and the Americans have done the same. The American trillion is 10^{12} and higher values rise stepwise by 10^3 instead of by 10^6 as with the British. This is apt to lead to confusion when American books are read in Britain or British books in America. It is advisable, therefore, when using values exceeding a million to write them also in figures to indicate which system is being used.

GEMATRIA

We cannot close this chapter without brief reference to that curious study known as gematria which concerns itself with what is known as the "power of words" as determined by the sum of the numerical values of their letters. It is an ancient study and dates back to the time of Pythagoras, some 550 B.C.; it began to be prominent about the 1st century A.D. The letters of the alphabet were given numbers and the power of a word was obtained by adding together the numbers of its component letters.

The letters of the Greek alphabet, for example, were given the following numbers—

Alpha	Beta	Gamma	Delta	Epsilon	Zeta	Eta
1	2	3	4	5	7	8

Theta	Iota	Kappa	Lambda	Mu	Nu	Xi
9	10	20	30	40	50	60

Omicron	Pi	Rho	Sigma	Tau	Upsilon
70	80	100	200	300	400

Phi	Chi	Psi	Omega
500	600	700	800

The mystic word *Abraxas*, indicating an amulet or engraved gem bearing a mystical figure often of combined human and animal form, adds up, in Greek gematria, to 365, representing the number of days in the year. The written word was supposed in consequence to ward off fever and pestilence for which purpose it was frequently written on parchment and enclosed in a small locket suspended from the neck.

In some early Christian manuscripts one finds 99 written at the end of a prayer; it signifies amen which in Greek gematria, has this word number, as the reader can easily confirm.

The letters used as numbers by the Romans were much pressed into service in the Middle Ages. Stiffel, the renowned German mathematician (1487–1567), argued that Pope Leo X was Antichrist, the Beast of *Revelation* 13, to which the number 666 had been allotted many centuries earlier. He arrived at his conclusion in this way—

The pope was Leo DeCIMVs or Leo X.

Rearranging the Roman numerals we obtain

MDCLXVI.

M, the initial letter of the Latin *mysterium*, signifies the mystery. Whence

The mystery of DCLXVI or 666.

Ridiculously farfetched, of course; but there it is. We do not now know how the number 666 was first obtained for the Beast. It may have been the gematrial number of some title given to Nero who, perhaps of all men, was the most hated by the early Christians.

One of the several schemes adopted for our own alphabet is as follows—

A	B	C	D	E	F	G	H	I or J
1	2	3	4	5	6	7	8	9

K	L	M	N	O	P	Q	R	S
10	20	30	40	50	60	70	80	90

T	U	V	W	X	Y	Z
100	110	120	130	140	150	160

Two different words possessing the same number are regarded as equivalent; having equal power. Thus—

$$AIR = DEAR = NO = PAIL = 90$$

Let us take a few examples from history and see how the scheme works out. It is very amusing; let those believe who choose to do so.

HAROLD 163
WILLIAM 219

One of the few dates we remember from childhood is "1066 and all that," when William the Norman had the temerity to invade England. Harold met him some six miles from Hastings and there ensued a terrific struggle in which the Saxon King was killed. Alas, the gematrial dice were heavily loaded against him. What could Harold's 163 do against William's 219? The result of the Battle of Hastings was a foregone conclusion; it would have saved much sorrow if it had never been fought.

NAPOLEON   266
WELLINGTON   421

Both Napoleon and Wellington were born in 1769, but it was not until 1815 that they actually fought against each other in person. The result was a fore-gone conclusion.

VICTORIA 372
ALBERT   208

When Queen Victoria was married in 1840 to Prince Albert, the question arose as to the desirabil-ity of omitting "obey" from the marriage ceremony. The Queen of England could not be required to obey any man. But no one need have worried; with a gematrial number of 372 the Queen could easily hold her own—and she did.

A similar question arose a few years ago; but those who care to work out the gematrial numbers of the Royal Persons involved will soon see that there is nothing to be anxious about.

NUMEROLOGY

It is well recognized that the health and happiness of the human race are closely connected with vibra-tions of one kind or another. Thus, when the amateur carpenter hits his thumb, instead of the nail at which he is aiming, he invariably drops his hammer and dances round, sucking the injured part. Primeval instinct tells him that the vibrations or waves induced by the dancing soothe the nerves and lessen the pain.

Aerial vibrations.or waves, which we call sound, likewise affect us. In ancient Hebrew days David would play his harp and soothe the ruffled nerves of Saul or, as the Old Testament puts it, cause the evil spirit to depart from him (I *Samuel* 16, 23). What wonder dancing and music played important roles in both medicine and religion.

But not all vibrations are soothing; some, like the screech of brakes, may be irritating even to the point of being painful; others, such as strains of martial music, may stir us into activity and lead to deeds of heroism. It is all a matter of what the scientist calls *frequency* or *wave number*, that is the number of waves passing a given point in unit time or the number in unit length respectively. To this extent we are influenced by numbers and different people respond differently to them according to the natural vibrations of their bodies. What is heaven to one may be agony to another, as witness different persons' reactions, for example, towards the barking of dogs, the crowing of the cock, the cacophony of jazz, and the like.

The student of numerology studies the various numerical relationships mentioned above. He claims that nothing happens by accident; it is not by mere chance that we are born, named and brought up. Each of us enters the world associated with certain sets of waves which are distinctive, complex and characteristic. Just as a mixture of sounds will produce harmony when the vibrations are in sympathy or dissonance when they are not, so our individual vibrations cause us to respond favorably or the reverse towards the people we meet or the circumstances in which we are placed. If their individual vibrations harmonize with ours, all is well; otherwise there is friction and incompatibility.

Our vibrations are in some way connected with the letters in our names or in those of objects connected with us. Hence in changing our names, as girls usually do upon marriage, new vibrations are induced which tend to redirect the mathematical influences that regulate our lives and control our thoughts, actions and health. For this reason a married woman usually develops into a very different kind of person from what she would have been had she remained in "single blessedness." Whether this is an improvement or not will depend upon the nature or wave numbers of the new vibrations.

Clearly we are masters of our fate to the extent, and to the extent only, that we can vary our wave numbers. We can thus appreciate the old Jewish custom of changing the name of a person sick unto death in the hope that the new vibrations thus induced would save his life. No doubt the change sometimes proved effective; psychology would see to that.

What the nature of the waves may be is not a matter that primarily concerns the numerologist; he is interested in their effects upon mankind, just as a man hurrying for his train is not primarily concerned with how his watch works but rather with the time it records.

The basic numbers of numerology are 1 to 9; higher numbers must in general be reduced to a single digit by adding up the constituent digits, thus 23 becomes 2 + 3 or 5. Following the ancient Chinese and Pythagorean suggestions, 1 is the male number, the vibration of self confidence and courage. It is the stuff that heroes are made of and is the associate of A, J and S. 2 is feminine and thus represents gentleness, ready adaptation to circumstances and love of peace; its letters are B, K and T.

To enumerate the qualities and letters associated with each of the other digits would lead us too far afield, but if these ideas are accepted it is obvious that a person's name, the date of his birth, the number of his house and indeed the names of the town, street and country in which he lives will each have a potent influence on his character, health, longevity and prospects.

Some of our natural numbers have been fixed for us beforehand, such as the date and place of our birth, and there is little we can do about them. It is open to us, however, if we wish, to change our names; more easily still we can change the street or town in which we live; it may be possible even to change our occupation. Thus, according to numerology, to a large extent our fate lies in our own hands, and it is up to us to direct it wisely.

X

NUMERICAL PROBLEMS

THIS chapter contains a number of problems, many of which are entirely new. A good many of them cannot be solved by recognized arithmetical and algebraical methods. They will thus tax the ingenuity of the reader who, we hope, will find them of considerable interest. The answers to these problems are given on pp. 189 to 193.

1. JOHN AND HIS DOG

One summer's day John left his school in the country to walk home. He had three miles to go and he passed through the playground gate at exactly half past four. At the same moment his dog left home to meet him. The boy walked at a steady rate of six kilometres per hour; not so the dog, which raced at an average of sixteen kilometres per hour. The dog met John and then ran back home, returned and met his young master and ran back home again. This went on until John reached home. How many kilometres did the dog run?

2. THE BUS NUMBER

One morning I carelessly left my umbrella in a local bus and did not miss it until next day. On notifying the lost-property office I was asked if I could by any chance remember the number of the bus. I couldn't, but I could remember being amused by the fact that the number was a perfect square and that if the number plate had been turned upside down, the number thus obtained would also have been a square. "That's sufficient," said the clerk with a smile, "We have 500 buses all told, so the number of your bus must have been . . ."

3. THE AWKWARD BATTALION

An officer had a battalion between 2000 and 3000 strong which he wished to divide into not more than nine smaller groups containing equal numbers of men. But by whatever digit he divided them there was always an odd man out. How many men were there?

4. THE SHOEMAKER

This is an old problem. A somewhat shady looking customer stopped to look in a shoemaker's window. It was raining at the time and the water was soaking through the shoddy footwear of the tramp. In the window lay a pair of boots marked 5 dollars which the tramp felt sure would fit him. Carefully caressing a ten dollar bill, as if wondering whether or not he dare part with it, he eventually made up his mind, entered the shop and asked for the boots. Receiving these in a brown paper parcel as usual he tendered his ten dollar bill in exchange. "Excuse me one moment, Sir," said the polite shoemaker, "I haven't sufficient change in my till but my neighbor will change your note for me. Won't be a second." The shoemaker returned in a few moments and handed his customer 5 dollars as change.

The customer left the shop with rather unusual haste—at least, so thought the shoemaker—and disappeared down the street as if hurrying for a train. A moment later the neighbor came rushing into the shop holding up the ten dollar bill and saying that it was a forgery; he wanted his money back. The poor shoemaker had perforce to give him a fresh, genuine ten dollar bill, after which he reported the matter to the police. The tramp, however, was never seen again.

How much did the shoemaker lose?

5. THE GROANING ASS

This is an ancient problem; the wording is that of Professor Robbins of Michigan.

A mule and an ass once went on their way with burdens of wine skins. Oppressed by the weight of her load, the ass was bitterly groaning. The mule, observing her grievous complaints, addressed her this question:

"Mother, why do you murmur with tears for a maiden more fitting?

For give me one measure of wine and twice your burden I carry;

But take one measure from me, and still you will keep our loads equal."

Tell me the measure they bore, good Sir, Geometry's Master.

6. THE NEW CARPETS

Joan had moved into a new house and decided to have new carpets for her front and back rooms. She selected two patterns of similar quality costing the same per square foot. The front room carpet measured three feet longer than it was broad; the back room carpet was one foot longer than the front one but one foot less in width and cost $8.00 less.

What did the carpets cost per square foot?

7. THE TWO FIELDS

"I have a field exactly a mile square" said Farmer George "and it cost me $2464 to have it fenced at 35¢ a yard." "Who'd a thowt it?" gasped Farmer Giles, "My field is also a square mile in area but although my fence cost only 28¢ a yard, I had to pay exactly the same as you." How did that come about?

8. THE SCHOOL-TIE CLUB

In one of the suburbs of London there was once an exclusive club for membership of which only men who had been to Eton or Harrow were eligible.

On examining the records on one occasion the President observed that 75 of the members were Etonians, 60 per cent. were Harrovians while 20 per cent. had attended both schools.

What was the total membership of the club?

9. HIS DAUGHTER'S AGE

Two old school friends were having coffee together when Tom remarked, "Your daughter's a fine girl; how old is she now?" "Her age," said John, "is given by reversing the figures of my own age. In ten years' time I shall be exactly twice as old as she will then be."

10. THOSE EGGS

This old problem has been served up from time to time in a variety of forms.

Mrs. Chick went to market with a basket of new-laid eggs collected from her own chickens that very morning. The eggs were such large ones and of such an attractive brown tint that Mrs. Chick was soon surrounded by eager customers. To the first of these she sold half her stock and half an egg more. To the second she sold half the remaining eggs and half an egg more. The third customer was treated in precisely the same way. Strange to say, in all these transactions not a single egg was broken.

It was now about noon, so Mrs. Chick cooked one of the eggs and had it with her sandwiches for lunch. Her stock now comprised 8 eggs which she soon disposed of, and wended her way cheerfully home.

How many eggs had Mrs. Chick in her basket when she left home that morning, and how much money did she take back with her having charged 7 cents per egg?

11. THE BENEVOLENT PASTOR

The Rev. Thomas Goodenough was one of the good old-fashioned sort. No one in distress ever appealed to him in vain, for his heart was full of the milk of human kindness. Of course he was often imposed upon as such good natured people are; but that made no difference. He loved his parishioners and they loved him.

One evening as he was wending his way home somewhat wearily, for he had had a heavy day, he met successively three needy persons who begged his help. He found that he had only coins in his pocket. To the first he gave half of what he had, and one penny over. To the second he again gave half of what was left and one penny over. To the third he gave half of what still remained and four pennies over. He thus reached home with only four pennies. How much had the worthy pastor to begin with?

12. A FAMILY PROBLEM

A man was talking to a friend about his son. "When I am as old as my father is now," said he, "I shall be four times my son's present age, but my son will then have reached my present age. It is a curious coincidence that my father's age, my son's and my own at the present moment add up to a century." The problem is to find the three ages.

13. ANOTHER FAMILY PROBLEM

My friend and I were taking coffee together. "You are rather fond of figures, aren't you?" he queried and, without waiting for a reply, he went on "My old schoolmaster, whom we affectionately nicknamed Old Dick, retired last year and went to live with his son Robert. Now it so happened that Robert was then exactly half his father's age and five times as old as his own son Herbert. In another five years Robert will be three times as old as Herbert will be. How old are all three now?"

14. THE HIKER

A young man who was fond of walking decided he would spend a pleasant Saturday in the country. He left the town on foot and by mid-day found himself in an attractive small village where he had lunch. This cost him half the money he had with him and in addition he left a tip of 10 cents. During the afternoon he walked on to another small town from which he could take a bus home. Having a little time to wait for the bus he went to a lunch counter and had some coffee and pie for which he paid half of his remaining money plus a five-cent tip. His bus fare cost seven-eighths of what was left and he had just 5 cents more with which to buy an evening paper. How much money did he have when he set out?

15. A LUNCHEON PARTY

Four young men went for a stroll into the country, and reaching a pretty little village about noon decided to have lunch together. Although their repast was modest, when the waiter handed them their bill they were hard put to find the money. By pooling their resources, however, they managed to pay as follows:

Eric paid 75¢ which was all he had.

Fred had just sufficient to pay his share, exclusive of the tip.

Tom was able to pay one-third of the whole bill,

while Harvey paid $2.00, which included a tip of a quarter for the waiter.

What was the total cost including the tip?

16. THE WINEBIBBERS

A happy party went into the country to enjoy the fresh air. After wandering over the hills under the hot sun they began to feel thirsty and finding a tavern with tables and seats laid out in the garden they wended their way thither to seek refreshment. There were 20 of them all told and they consumed 20 pennyworth of wine. When it was time to leave, each man paid 3 pence, each woman 2 pence and each girl one halfpenny. How many of each were present?

17. THE SAILORS' SPREE

Six happy sailors from the *Saucy Araminta* spent eight hours' leave in Liverpool, visiting cinemas, cafes and having a good time generally. On returning to the ship and recounting their experiences it transpired that five of the sailors, all married men, had each spent twenty shillings, but that the sixth man, Jim Salt, who was a bachelor and free from encumbrances, had spent five shillings more than the average for them all. The problem is—how much did Jim actually spend?

18. THE FARMER'S BARGAIN

Farmer Giles went to market and bought some sheep and cows to the total value of $848. Each cow cost 8 times as much as a sheep, and there were 25 animals all told. Assuming no fractions of a dollar were involved, how many sheep and cows were purchased, and what was the price of each?

19. FATHER AND SON

I am 30 years older than my son. If my son's age is placed before mine the four digit number thus obtained is a perfect square. In twenty-five years' our ages will similarly form a four digit square. What are our ages?

20. SIR WALTER RALEIGH'S RIDE

At one time Sir Walter Raleigh was a great favourite of Queen Elizabeth I. His wit, genius and undoubted courage, coupled with a fine physique and a certain degree of audacity, greatly impressed the Virgin Queen. So considerable was his influence that Tarleton, the comedian, once ventured to say in front of his royal mistress, "See, the knave commands the queen."

In 1587 Raleigh had become captain of the Queen's Guard, and was one day out hunting some little distance from London when he received an urgent summons to present himself before Her Majesty at the Tower at precisely 4 P.M.

Sir Walter indulged in a little mental arithmetic. If he left the field now and trotted at 4 miles per hour he would reach the Tower at 3 P.M. which would give him ample time to repair his attire before meeting the queen. He might, however, enjoy another two hours' hunting if he then galloped at

8 miles per hour, for he would still reach the Tower at
3 o'clock in the afternoon. This he therefore decided
to do. How far had he to travel?

21. THE HUNDRED BIRDS

This problem is adapted from one found in an
Indian manuscript of *c*. 850 A.D.

An Indian prince had an only son. It was holiday
time and the problem arose as to how the young
Rajah was to be amused in order to keep him out of
mischief. The prince therefore called his chief
servant and instructed him to go to the market and
purchase 100 birds and bring them back with him.
He was at liberty to buy what birds he liked, but
must pay only 100 rupees. The servant did as he was
bid, purchasing pigeons at the rate of 5 for 3 rupees,
larks at 7 for 5 rupees and parrots at 3 for 9 rupees.
The total bag of birds cost exactly 100 rupees. How
many of each were there? No fractions of a rupee
were involved.

22. HER HUSBAND'S INCOME

Young Betsy Smith had been married to Jim for
three years and often wondered what her husband's
income was. A wise fellow was Jim; he kept that
information to himself. He did, however, confide in
Betsy that so far they had spent 40 per cent. of his
salary on the upkeep of the house, 25 per cent. on
food and clothing, while incidentals absorbed another
10 per cent. He was thus able to save 25 per cent.
One fatal day Jim forgot to lock his desk and Betsy,

with typical feminine curiosity, looked inside and saw his bankbook. Opening it she found that Jim had saved $3000—quite a respectable sum. This enabled her to estimate her husband's income. What was it?

23. MARY'S AGE

Mary had a black and white spaniel of which she was inordinately fond. It could do no wrong. One day it stole a piece of beef from the local butcher's shop for which the butcher demanded payment. "Not on your life," said Mary, "it was entirely your fault for leaving the meat lying about." In due course Mary was summoned and when she appeared in court the magistrate's clerk amongst other things, asked her age. At first she refused to divulge so intimate a secret, but finally after being warned of divers penalties if she remained obdurate, she said "Fact is, I don't rightly know, yer honour. But I do remember my father remarking on my last birthday that I was just six times as old as Vic, whereas four years ago I was eleven times as old. As yer honour is a scholar mebbe ye can work that out for yer self. As for me, I dinna ken what the answer is." Can you guess?

24. SHOES FOR THE EX-SERVICE MEN

Christmas was drawing near and the owners of the local Gazette in the town of Treatemwell had opened up a fund for purchasing shoes for the town's needy ex-service men. The number of men on the rolls was 200 and one of the newspaper staff was

detailed to find out how many separate shoes (not
pairs) would be required. On examining the records
he found that 5 per cent. of the men had only one
leg each, having lost the other in the War, while
50 per cent. of the remaining men were in good
circumstances and did not need the shoes. How
many shoes were required?

25. THE ELDERLY RIDDELLS

The pastor was new to the village and when he
made his first call on elderly Mr. and Mrs. Riddell
he was made very welcome. Elderly people are often
very proud of their age and this sturdy couple was
no exception.

"How old do ye think we be, my wife and me,
Mr. White?" asked the old man.

"I really don't know" replied the pastor angling
for time to think out a complimentary reply. "Mrs.
Riddell looks very young yet; I will put her at 50;
and you, sir, well, you might easily pass for 60."

"You be flattering us as ye very well know, Sir,"
said the delighted Mr. Riddell with a twinkle in his
eye. "We baint that young. But I will gie thee a
clue. Both my wife's age and mine read the same
when turned upside down. Also, sir, if the differences
between our ages be also turned upside down it gives
my wife's age of eight years agone. Now, sir, can ye
reckon that out?"

The pastor enjoyed his visit and promised to tell
the elderly couple what their ages were when next he
called. He kept his promise.

26. THE ARITHMETICAL CONSTABLE

It was a dark, moonless night when Police Constable Catch M. Quick took shelter from the torrential rain under a suburban railways arch. He was known in the force as the Arithmetical Constable for he was never more happy than when plaguing his colleagues with mathematical problems of which he had a rare collection taken from all sorts of books and papers.

The constable yawned and shook his watch to make sure that it was going. The night seemed interminably long and monotonously quiet when suddenly he pricked up his ears. What was that? It sounded like a thud and a groan. Proceeding in the direction of the sound he saw a car approaching rapidly. "Better take its number," thought he, "just in case . . . " As the car got within range he read the letters CM. "That's easy," he commented aloud, "for those are my own initials—and now for the number—why, that's peculiar!"

On he walked and presently, flashing his lamp, saw an elderly man slowly rising to his feet on the footpath. "What's up, Chum?" he asked kindly. "Tripped up getting out of the way of that car; it was going mighty fast." "Hurt?" "No thanks. A bit shaken at first, but think I shall be all right now. Good night, constable."

Subsequently as P.C. Quick was writing up his official account of the incident he could not for the life of him remember the number of the car. He did however recollect that there were four different digits including the cipher and that if these were added together, their sum squared and the result squared again, the number of the car was obtained.

"That's simple," he said and, after jotting a few figures on an odd piece of scrap-paper, he completed his report in a couple of minutes. What was the number of the car?

27. BOBBY PEEL

Young Bobby Peel had recently joined the city police force; he was full of enthusiasm and hoped for rapid promotion for he had had a college education and felt a notch above the ordinary rank and file.

It was a summer's evening and people were hurrying home both on foot and in their cars by the thousand; it was sultry and a thunderstorm seemed imminent. Robert, on point duty, noticed that one car was rapidly overtaking and passing all others although it was a built up area with a speed limit of 30 m.p.h. As the car flashed by him he noticed that the number comprised four digits and had two peculiarities; it was a perfect square, and if the number-plate had been turned upside down the number would still have read the same. What was the number?

28. BETTY SHARP'S BUS TICKET

Betty Sharp was as alert as her name implied. For nearly 20 years she had been confidential clerk to Messrs. Dry Brothers, Solicitors, of Desert

Chambers, Stingemwell. Her day's work was done and she was travelling home in the bus. When she received her ticket she looked at its number and then at that of the conductor. It so happened that both of them contained two digits and in addition both were squares. If she placed the bus number in front of that of the conductor a four digit square was obtained. The square root of this latter number was Betty Sharp's age. How old was Betty?

29. ENGINE NUMBERS

James Watt was keen on engines and on everything connected with them, even their numbers, of which he was a rabid collector. His father was an equally enthusiastic collector of postage stamps. He thought that his son's energies were grossly misplaced, that the collection of mere engine numbers led nowhere, whereas the study of stamps was not merely interesting but instructive and could even be exciting.

James maintained that his collection cost nothing and was also educative. "See, Dad," he said one day, "this morning I saw four new engines and took their numbers. Each number had four digits including the cipher; all were squares and two of them were each exactly nine times the other two respectively. The same digit does not occur twice in any one number. What are the numbers, Dad?"

Dad thought awhile then, looking at the clock, suggested that it was high time James went to bed. James said nothing, but thought the more. Could you solve the problem?

30. THE BIRMINGHAM CYCLIST

Charley Wheeler was heading for Birmingham on his penny-farthing boneshaker. Arrived at Warwick he asked a police-constable how much further he had to go. The stout up-holder of the Law replied, with a twinkle in his eye, "Well, Sir, mebbe ye'll be able to work it out for yerself if I tell ye that if ye square the distance and divide by 5, the result will be 80."

"Thanks so much" said the cyclist "I guess it'll take me 2½ hours." How great was the distance and how fast did the cyclist travel?

31. THE COAL PROBLEM

Mr. Byrne was lunching with Professor Figaro, who held the chair of mathematics at the local university and was regarded as the city's most remarkable lightning calculator. "Last week," said Mr. Byrne, "the miners in our area dug up a record number of tons of coal. I can't remember the exact figure; it was rather more than half a million and I did notice that its square root and cube root were whole numbers." "That's interesting," said the professor and a few moments later added, "there is only one number between half a million and a million like that; it must be . . . " he wrote on a slip of paper and handed it to his friend. "That's it exactly," exclaimed Mr. Byrne in astonishment, "how on earth did you find it out?"

32. THE CHESSBOARD

The game of chess is supposed to have been invented by the Chinese long ago. A very old story says that when the game was explained to the king, he was so delighted that he told the inventor to ask for any reward he pleased. The inventor modestly asked that he be given a grain of wheat for the first square on the chessboard, 2 grains for the second square, 4 for the third, 8 for the fourth, and so, doubling each time.

The old story points out that no emperor could ever hope to foot that bill. Why not?

33. THE HORSE-SHOE

A variant of the chessboard problem is found in manuscripts of the 15th and 16th centuries. In an Italian manuscript of c.1535 a blacksmith agrees to shoe a horse if he receives one "penny" (to anglicise it) for the first nail, two for the second, four for the third and so on. There were 24 nails in all. What was the total reward?

34. THE 12345 PUZZLE

The difference between the squares of two whole numbers is 12345. What are the numbers?

35. THE DUKE'S FIELD

Taxes being ruinous the Duke decided to sell some of his land. He had a square field which a farmer was anxious to purchase but could not agree with the agents as to the true size of the field. He maintained that its side was one yard shorter than the agents had advertised and that its area was in consequence some 35 square yards less. What was the advertised area of the field?

36. THE SQUARED BATTALION

After a skirmish an officer marched his men, numbering approximately 1,000, back to headquarters in the form of a square. On the way ten men fell out as casualties during the first mile, so he re-formed his men into six squares. During the second mile six more men fell out, so the officer arranged the remainder of his battalion in seven squares. How many men had he when he reported at HQ?

37. THE HINDU MERCHANT

Here is another old problem which is undoubtedly of Hindu origin and may easily date back to the 9th century.

A merchant set out on his travels to a distant city with a load of goods. He had perforce to stay the night at two different cities en route and was compelled to pay customs duty on each occasion. The duty was paid in kind, but we are only concerned with the value in lakhs.

At the first city he had to give up one-third of his goods; at the second, one-quarter of what he had left. On reaching his destination he was mulcted of one-fifth of the remainder. If the total duty paid was the equivalent of 24 lakhs what was the initial value of his goods?

38. THE YOUNG PHILATELISTS

The two brothers Harold and Edward were keen collectors. When their uncle came home after serving in the Pacific he gave them 100 postage stamps. Now it so happened that if the number allotted to Harold had been increased by one third, it would have been equal to the square root of the product of the numbers of stamps received by each of the boys. How many stamps did Harold actually receive?

39. THE LOCAL CENSUS

"When the local census was taken a short time ago," said Mr. Figaro to his friend over a morning cup of coffee, "it was noticed that the population of this town was given by a five-digit number which read the same when turned upside down; it was moreover a perfect square. Can you tell me what it was?"

40. ANOTHER CENSUS STORY

It was nine o'clock and the boys had assembled for their lesson in arithmetic, the teacher believing that the best time to hold classes in mathematics is the morning when everyone is fresh and alert.

"You will remember, boys," the teacher began, "that a few days ago a local census was taken, when it was found that our population is represented by a square number comprising five digits of two kinds which we can represent by *ababa*. The sum of the digits *b* is the same as that of digits *a*. What is the population?"

XI

PROBLEMS
WITH DIGITS AND LETTERS

Hitherto we have been concerned mainly with digits. Let us now consider a few problems in which some or all of the digits have been replaced by letters. Such problems cannot in general be solved "according to rule," they demand a considerable amount of thought and mental ingenuity. The reader will, we believe, find them peculiarly fascinating. Solutions to the problems not solved in the text will be found on p. 193.

1. Here is a neat little problem. a, b, c and d represent four different digits. Given that
$$(ab)^3 = c\,a\,d\,b$$
and $(cd)^2 = c\,a\,b\,d$
find the numerical equivalents of a, b, c and d.

To begin with, it is clear that since the cube of 22 has five digits, namely 10648, $(ab)^3$ cannot exceed $(21)^3$. Further, as the cube of ab also ends in b, the value of b is limited to 1, 4, 5, 6 and 9. Possible values for ab are thus 14, 15, 16, 19 and 21. Of these, 21 alone fits the equation, so that

$$(ab)^3 = (21)^3 = 9261$$
$$\text{and } (cd)^2 = (96)^2 = 9216$$

2. Given that $(bc)^2 = a\,b\,c$, we are asked to find the appropriate digits.

This is easy if we remember the rule that only numbers ending in 25 and 76 yield powers ending in the same digits. Hence bc must be either 25 or 76, and trial shows it to be the former.

If, however, we overlook this rule, the problem still admits of easy solution. Let us multiply out in the usual way:

$$
\begin{array}{r}
bc \\
bc \\
\hline
xxc \\
xx \\
\hline
abc
\end{array}
$$

x here represents any digit including o. Clearly c can only be 1, 5 or 6, whilst bc cannot exceed 31, since the square of 32 involves four digits (1024). Possible values for bc are thus 15, 16, 21, 25, 26 and 31. Of these 25 is the only one to satisfy the above conditions.

3. Given that $(abc)^2 = bcdbc$, let us find the digits. The number abc cannot be greater than 316, otherwise its square would comprise six digits for $317^2 = 100489$. Furthermore, since the square of abc ends in bc, bc can only be 25 or 76. abc must therefore be one of the following numbers, 125, 176 or 276. Trial shows that abc is the last of these since $(276)^2 = 76176$.

4. In the following problem even the index is denoted by a letter. We are asked to find the digits that will satisfy the equation

$(ab)^c = cdb$

Obviously c cannot be 0 or 1, since $(ab)^0 = 1$ and $(ab)' = ab$. Also c cannot exceed 2 since $10^3 = 1000$ and $(ab)^c$ yields only a three-digit number. Our equation thus simplifies to

$(ab)^2 = 2db$

Since $(ab)^2$ lies between 200 and 300, a can only be 1. Furthermore since the square of ab also ends in b, b can only be 5 or 6. Trial shows it to be the latter. Thus $16^2 = 256$.

5. Here is a slightly more complicated problem. Let us find the numerical values of a, b, c, d and e when

$(ed)^b = ebad$
$(cd)^b = abed$
$(ba)^c = ebda$

Since $10^4 = 10,000$, neither b nor c can exceed 3. As neither can be 0 or 1, they must be 2 and 3 or 3 and 2 respectively. Since $(ba)^c$ yields a number $ebda$ whose final digit is a, it follows that, when $c = 2$, $b = 3$ and $a = 1$, 5 or 6. When $c = 3$, $b = 2$ and $a = 1$, 4, 5, 6 or 9. Values of $(ba)^c$ are thus limited to $(35)^2$, $(36)^2$ and $(21)^3$. Higher values such as $(24)^3$ etc. are ruled out as they yield numbers comprising more than four digits, whilst $(31)^2$ yields only a three digit number. Trial shows that $(21)^3$ meets the requirements. The rest is easy.

6. Here are a few more similar problems:

  (i) $(cc)^2 = bbaa$ (ii) $(aaa)^2 = abcba$
  (iii) $a + d = 9$; $cbca = (da)^2$;
    $c + b + c + a = ad$
  (iv) $(acd)^2 = aebbd$; $(bed)^2 = eabbd$
  (v) $(db)^2 = bcab$; $(bab)^2 = adbcab$
  (vi) $(ed)^2 = ceed$; $(ed)^3 = bafged$

7. This is a simple addition sum involving all nine digits (the cipher is excluded):

$a\ b\ 9$
$c\ 1\ d$
_____
$5\ e\ f$

Clearly a and c must be 2 and 3 respectively, or 3 and 2, it doesn't matter which. We thus obtain scheme (i). Again d must exceed 3; it cannot be 4 or 6 as these would make $f = 3$ or 5 both of which digits have already been fixed; d can thus be only 7 or 8. As 7 proves impossible, d must be 8 and the rest is easy. We thus arrive at scheme (ii). The interchange of 2 and 3 gives the only other possible solution shown in scheme (iii).

$2\ b\ 9$ $2\ 4\ 9$ $3\ 4\ 9$
$3\ 1\ d$ $3\ 1\ 8$ $2\ 1\ 8$
_____   _____   _____
$5\ e\ f$ $5\ 6\ 7$ $5\ 6\ 7$
  (i)   (ii)   (iii)

8. Sums involving division may be very difficult. Here is a relatively simple problem.
Given that f is an even digit, find the
solution for

$$a\,b)\,c\,d\,e\,e\,b\,(b\,f\,b$$
$$\underline{c\,e\,b}$$
$$g\,g\,e$$
$$\underline{g\,c\,h}$$
$$c\,e\,b$$
$$\underline{c\,e\,b}$$

There are ten letters, so that one of them
must represent o. As the subtraction of h
from e in the third line leaves e in the fifth,
h must be o. As $f \times b$ in line 4 gives a number ending in o, b must be 5 since f is even.
e in line 2 must therefore be either 2 or 7
according as a is even or odd. If $e = 2$,
g must be 7 which makes $d = 0$, which is
impossible as $h = 0$. Taking $e = 7$, g becomes 2 and $d = 9$. We have now reached
scheme (i) below:

$$a\,5)\,c\,9\,7\,7\,5\,(5\,f\,5$$
$$\underline{c\,7\,5}$$
$$2\,2\,7$$
$$\underline{2\,c\,o}$$
$$c\,7\,5$$
$$\underline{c\,7\,5}$$

The rest is easy; $a = 3$, $c = 1$ and $f = 6$.

9. Here by way of a change is a simple multiplication sum in which x may represent any digit:

```
      3 4 5
        x x
    ---------
    x x x x
  x x x x
  -----------
  x x 7 6 x
```

10. The following addition sums are, to say the least, amusing. As before, each letter represents a digit.

(i)	SEND	(ii)	HAVE	(iii)	THREE	(iv)	WOOD	(v)	CROSS
	MORE		SOME		FOUR		JOHN		ROADS
	MONEY		HONEY		SEVEN		HANTS		DANGER

It is rumoured that a letter was once dropped into the post with the envelope bearing the fourth puzzle. After a slight delay the letter was delivered to

John *Under*wood
Andover
Hants.

11. The following represent subtractions.

(i)	SANTA	(ii)	NINE	(iii)	SPEND
	CLAUS		FOUR		MORE
	XMAS		FIVE		MONEY

XII

PROBLEMS
WITH MATCHES AND COINS

It is remarkable what a lot of fun can be obtained by playing with match sticks and coins. Solutions to the problems will be found on p. 194.

1. You are given nine matches arranged as follows:

By taking away two matches make the equation correct.

2. The above is easy. Now here are six matches:

By moving (not removing) two matches the equation may be made correct.

3. These fourteen matches obviously portray an untruth. By moving only one match you can render the

statement correct.

4. By moving two matches correct this very obvious falsehood:

5. Arrange six matches in such a manner as to indicate 1050.

6. With six matches describe a hexagon. From this figure by moving two matches and adding one extra match you can obtain two diamonds.

7. You are given nine matches. Try and make ten of them.

8. Given eight matches you are asked to take away three and still leave eight.

9. Here are nine matches arranged in the form of three triangles. The problem is to re-arrange the matches, by moving three only, to yield five triangles.

10. Given twelve matches, arrange them in such a manner as to yield six equal triangles.

11. Fifteen matches are arranged in the form

of six squares. Can you, by removing three only, halve the number of squares?

12. Here are ten matches arranged to enclose a T-shaped area. Given two more matches arrange them to enclose exactly twice the area.

13. Eighteen matches are arranged to form Solomon's Seal or the hexalpha (p. 130), which comprises a hexagon and eight triangles.

By merely moving two matches reduce the number of triangles to six.

14. Here are sixteen matches arranged as a gnomon. Given eight more matches divide the area into four equal and similarly shaped areas without disturbing any of the sixteen matches shown.

15. Here are eight matches:

1 2 3 4 5 6 7 8

We are asked to make four crosses in a like number of moves, picking up one match at a time and passing it over two others before laying it crosswise on the next match.

16. Coins are a never ending source of amusement. Here are six coins arranged in two rows. It is easy enough, by moving two coins, to form a ring. All we have to do is to

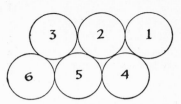

move 5 to touch 6 only, and bring 1 down to touch 4 and 5. But can you form a ring in three moves?

17. Here are nine pennies. The problem is to arrange them in ten rows, each row containing three pennies.

18. Now take an extra penny and arrange the ten coins in five rows, each row to contain four pennies.

19. Place eight pennies in a row:

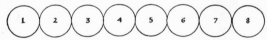

The problem is to arrange these in four pairs in a like number of moves. Only one penny may be moved at a time and before it takes up its position by the side of another penny it must have passed two other pennies, and two only.

20. *The heavy dollar.* "See, Michael," said the boy's Father, "here are twelve dollar pieces

minted in different years. Eleven of them are the same weight, but the twelfth is slightly heavier. Now here is an accurate balance and, if you can single out the heavy coin in not more than three weighings, the money is yours." "Right, Dad," said Michael, "I'll do my best." In a short time he handed his father the heavy coin. How do you think he found it?

21. There is a trick in this problem. You are given a bowl and two cups. The bowl holds six pennies and you are required to arrange matters so that the bowl and each of the cups hold an odd number of pennies.

APPENDIX

APPENDIX

PROLOGUE

$$I = \sqrt{1}$$

Although the expression

$$I \neq VI$$

is mathematically correct, it is not the solution to the problem because it is not an equation.

CHAPTER IV	(1) 169
	(2) Edward 47, Mrs. Prime 41, John 13
	(3) Pat 73, Mike 37
	(4) Postman 61, Son 31, Charlie 7
	(5) 36481
CHAPTER V	(6) If the woman had sold all 600 apples at 5 for 20¢ the first 500 would have contained all the cheaper apples and 200 of the dearer, leaving 100 of the dearer to be sold at this lower rate instead of 5¢ each, the difference being $1.00
CHAPTER VI	p. 83 85 feet. The diameter of the log makes no difference
CHAPTER VIII	p. 110 1881

NUMERICAL PROBLEMS

| CHAPTER X | (1) 8 miles or 16 kilometres |
| | (2) 196 |

(3) The product $5 \times 7 \times 8 \times 9$ plus 1, namely 2521

(4) The shoemaker's loss was the customer's gain, namely 5 dollars and a pair of boots.

(5) Mule 7, ass 5.

(6) $2.00.

(7) The second field was rectangular, 2 miles long and ½ mile broad.

(8) 150.

(9) Father 62, daughter 26.

(10) 79 eggs. $5.46.

(11) 70 cents.

(12) Grandfather 53⅓, 33⅓, boy 13⅓.

(13) Dick 61, Robert 31, Herbert 7.

(14) $2.00.

(15) $6.25.

(16) 1 man, 5 women, 14 girls.

(17) 26 s.

(18) Cow $128, Sheep $16, 4 cows, 21 sheep.

(19) Father 44, son 14.

(20) 16 miles.

(21) 50 pigeons, 35 larks, 15 parrots.

(22) $4000.

(23) 48.

(24) 200.

(25) Mr. Riddell 88, Mrs. Riddell 69.

(26) 2401.

(27) 6889.

(28) 41.

(29) 1024, 1089, 9216, 9801.

(30) 20 miles at 8 mph.

(31) 531,441.

(32) As there are 64 squares on the chess-

board, the number of grains required would be $2^{64} - 1$ or rather more than 18 trillion (18×10^{18}).

(33) The total reward was $2^{24}-1$ pence or 16,777,215, equivalent to nearly £70,-000 or $195,000—quite a handsome amount.

(34) 1237 and 1232.

(35) 375,769 square yards.

(36) 1008.

(37) 40 lakhs.

(38) 36.

(39) 69169.

(40) This problem was quickly solved. As $2b = 3a$, a must be even. As no square ends in 2 or 8, a can only be 4 or 6 and b in consequence 6 or 9. The population could thus be either 46464 or 69696. Of these only the latter is a square and is therefore the desired number.

DIGITS AND LETTERS

6. (i) $88^2 = 7744$. (ii) $111^2 = 12321$.
    (iii) $a = 1, b = 5, c = 6, d = 8$.
    (iv) $135^2 = 18225$; $285^2 = 81225$.
    (v) $75^2 = 5625$; $525^2 = 275625$.
    (vi) $76^2 = 5776$; $76^3 = 438976$.

9. 345×37

10. (i) $9567 + 1085$. (ii) $1386 + 9076$.
    (iii) $79422 + 3104$. (iv) $8776 + 3714$.
    (v) $96233 + 62513$.

11. (i) $24794 - 16452$, or $36156 - 28693$.
    (ii) $5456 - 2980$. (iii) $70839 - 6458$.

MATCHES AND COINS

1. Remove V then II − I = I

2. $\dfrac{I}{I} = I$

3. VII − $\sqrt{I}$ = VI
4. VII − V = II

5.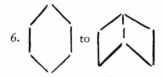

6.

7.

8. VIII

9.

10.

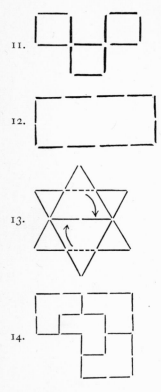

11.

12.

13.

14.

15. Move the matches in the following order: 5 on 2, 3 on 7, 1 on 4 and 8 on 6. Alternatively 4 on 7, 6 on 2, 1 on 3 and 8 on 5.

16. Move 4 to touch 5 and 6; 5 to touch 1 and 2; 1 to touch 4 and 5.

17.

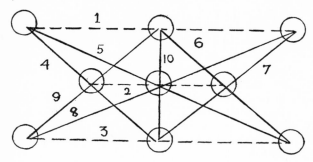

18. The pennies are arranged to form a wizard's pentagon
(p. 128). Five lines of four coins each are easily seen.

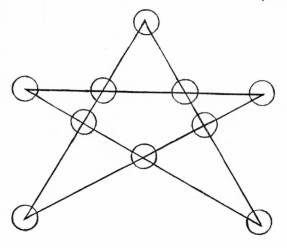

19. Move the pennies in the following order: 4 to 7, 6 to 2, 1 to 3 and 8 to 5. Alternatively from 5 to 2, 3 to 7, 1 to 4 and 8 to 6.

20. Michael divided the dollars into three sets of four each. The first two balanced exactly, so he knew that the third set contained the heavier coin. Had the two not balanced he would just as easily detected the heavier set. The rest was easy.

21. Place one penny in one cup and three in the other. The basin now holds two pennies but by placing the cup with it one penny in the basin, the latter now holds three. Each vessel now holds an odd number of pennies.

BOOKS RECOMMENDED
FOR FURTHER STUDY

AARON BAKST, *Mathematics; Its Magic and Mastery*, Van Nostrand, New York, 1941.

W. W. ROUSE BALL, *Mathematical Recreations and Essays*, Revised by H. S. M. Coxeter, Macmillan, New York, 1939.

H. E. DUDENEY, *The Canterbury Puzzles*, Nelson, New York, 1921.

————, *Amusements in Mathematics*, Nelson, London, 1946.

G. F. HILL, *Development of Arabic Numerals in Europe*, Oxford University Press, New York, 1915.

LANCELOT, HOGBEN, *Mathematics for the Million*, Norton, New York, 1943.

P. E. B. JOURDAIN, *The Nature of Mathematics*, Jack and Nelson, London, 1919.

E. KASNER and J. R. NEWMAN, *Mathematics and the Imagination*, Simon and Schuster, New York, 1940.

D. N. LEHMER, *List of Prime Numbers 1 to 10,006,721*, Carnegie Institution, Washington, No. 165, 1914.

D. E. SMITH, *History of Mathematics*, Ginn, New York, Volume I, 1923, Volume II, 1925.

MELIUS DE VILLIERS, *The Numeral Words*, Witherby, London, 1923.

INDEX

INDEX

Abacus, 8
Abraham, 119, 143
Abraxas, 151
Abstract Numbers, 36 ff.
Absurdities, 68
Achilles, 1, 74
Al Kashi, 51
Al Khwarāzmi, 25, 49
Alchemists, 119
Alexander the Great, 126, 144
Algorithm, 25
Ali Baba, 148
Alice, 1, 77
All Fools' Day, 115
Amicable Numbers, 36
Ancestor Problem, 74
Anti-Christ, 152
Apollo's Problem, 86
Apple Problem, 71
Arabian Nights, 105, 115
Archimedes, 52
Aristotle, 126
Arithmetical Constable, 170
  Sieve, 42
Atonement Day, 142
Awkward Battalion Problem, 159

Baker's Dozen, 144, 147
Balaam, 1, 119
Bantus, 18
Barleyfield Problem, 72
Bath, The, 142
Beast, Number of the, 21, 152
Bee's Number, 130
Beheaded Numbers, 78
Benevolent Pastor, 162
Benjamin, 129
Bergholt's Square, 99
Betrothal Ring, 9
Betty Sharp's Problem, 171

Big Ben, 19, 20
  Brum, 20
Billion, 150
Birmingham Cyclist Problem, 173
Bobby Peel, 171
Book of Permutations, 112
Bruce, Robert, 137
Buffon's Needle Problem, 53
Bus Number Problem, 158
Byron, 144

Calculator, 6
Candles, 120, 121, 127, 130
Cardan, 40
Cardinal Numbers, 35 ff.
Casting out Nine, 63
Castor and Pollux, 117, 133
Census Problems, 176
Ceulen, van, 51
Chessboard Problem, 174
Christ, 120, 138, 143, 145–148
Chuquet, 150
Cipher, 24, 31
Cities of Refuge, 120
Clock Faces, 19
Clover, 123
  Four-leaved, 127
Clubs, 123
Coal Problem, 173
Codex Vigilanus, 26
Coin Problems, 186 ff.
Coincidences, 54
Columbus, 118
Commandments, 143
Computing Rods, 27
Concrete Numbers, 36 ff.
Counting, 11 ff.
  Basis of, 14
  Primitive, 3
  Unnamed, 4

[203]

Cribrum Arithmeticum, 42
Cube Roots, 89 ff.
Cubes, 85 ff.
  Magic, 100
Cubit, 51
Curiosities, 81
Curious Numbers, 62 ff.
Curse of Scotland, 141

Daughter's Age Problem, 161
David, 129, 149, 155
Decalogue, 143
Decemviri, 142
Decimal System, 15
Deluge, The, 135
Denary System, 15
Dickens, 32
Digit, 12
Digital Fractions, 59
  Root, 40
  Triangle, 59
Digits, The, 34 ff., 55 ff.
Dozen, 15, 144, 147
Druids, 123, 130
Dual System, 4
Dudeney's Square, 99
Duke's Field Problem, 174
Duodecimal System, 15
Duplation, 32
Dürer's Square, 98

Eclipses, 134
Edible Number, 50 ff.
Egg Problem, 162
Eight, 30, 138 ff.
Elderly Riddells Problem, 169
Eleven, 15, 45, 103, 143 ff.
Elijah, 122, 146
Elisha, 132, 146
Ell, 11
Engine Numbers Problem, 172
Ephah, 142
Epiphany Service, 121
Eratosthenes, 42
Euler's Equation, 43
  Rule, 128

Even Numbers, 34, 112
Evil Eye, 97, 111, 127, 128, 130
Exchequer Office, 9, 10
Excommunication, 120

Fair Ticket Problem, 49
Fallacies, 68 ff.
Family Problems, 47, 163
Farmer's Bargain, 165
Father and Son Problem, 166
Feline Number, 140
Female Numbers, 34, 112, 157
Fermat, Pierre de, 36, 85
Five, 14 ff., 18, 29, 127 ff.
Fives, A Bunch of, 127
Fonts, 126, 138
Forty, 148
  Winks, 148
Four, 28, 126 ff.
Freaks, 81
Frequency, 155
Furlong, 12

Geikie, 77
Gematria, 151 ff.
Googal, 92
Googalplex, 92
Great Bear, 117, 134
Greek Priest, 7
Gregorian Calendar, 116
Groaning Ass Problem, 160
Group Number, 14

Hand, 12, 15, 34, 141
Hangman's Fee, 148
Hannah, 142
Harold, 153
Heavy Dollar Problem, 187
Hermes, 124, 126
Herschel, 133
Hexalpha, 130
Hickson, 125
Higher Powers, 90 ff.
Hiker Problem, 164
Hindu Merchant Problem, 175
Hood, Tom, 34

Hoppenot's Rule, 84
Horseshoe, 132
    Problem, 174
Hottentots, 4
Hundred, 19, 58, 81, 89
    Birds Problem, 167
Husband's Income Problem, 167

I-king, 112
Imaginary Numbers, 38 ff.
Imperfect Numbers, 41
In Bread, 147
Inch, 12
Incommensurable Numbers, 49 ff.
Indefinite Numbers, 124, 129, 138,
    139, 142, 144, 148, 149
Integers, 35

Jacob, 129, 135, 146
Jericho, 136
Jerome, Jerome K., 125
John and His Dog Problem, 158
Johnson, Dr., 121
Jonah, 120
Joseph, 119, 129, 135
Joshua, 146
Jury, 144

Kasner, 92
Knotted Cords, 10, 11

Langland, 150
Last Supper, 147
Lazzarini, 54
Letter Problems, 177 ff.
Library Book Problem, 110
Lichfield, 121
Lo Shu, 96 ff.
Lover, Samuel, 113
Lucas, Edouard, 44
Luncheon Party Problem, 164
Lutine Bell, 115
Lyre, 143

Macaulay, 117, 139, 149
Macbeth, 121

Magi, 121, 145
Magic Cubes, 100
    Squares, 94 ff.
Magpie, 114
Malaria, 144
Male Numbers, 34, 112, 157
Mary's Age Problem, 168
Match Problems, 183 ff.
Mau Mau, 137
Mayan Numeration, 14
Michelangelo, 114
Million, 149
Milton, 124
Mnemonics for π, 52 ff.
Multiplication, Roman, 21
    Simple, 22

Naaman, 132
Napoleon, 101, 266
Nehemiah, 142
Nero, 152
New Carpets Problem, 160
Newton, Sir Isaac, 17, 133
Nicksticks, 8
Nimble Ninepence, 140
Nine, 31, 62 ff., 107, 139
    Days' Wonder, 140
    of Diamonds, 141
    Pins, 140
    Tail Bruiser, 140
    Tailors, 141
    The, 139
Noah, 135, 138
Nought, 31
Novosiles, 139
Number Palindromes, 101 ff.
    Sense, 2 ff.
    Squares, 95 ff.
Numerals, Hindu-Arabic, 25 ff.
    Mayan, 14
    Origin of, 16 ff.
    Roman, 16 ff.
Numerical Problems, 158 ff.
Numerical System, Ideal, 23
    Roman, 17
Numerology, 154 ff.

Odd Numbers, 34, 112
Oddities, 58
Odds and Evens, 112
Old Curiosity Shop, 55 ff.
One, 17, 27, 35, 114 ff.
One-eyed Man, 114
One to One Correspondence 5 ff.
Ordeal, 120
Ordinal Numbers, 35 ff.
Over-perfect Numbers, 41

Palindromes, Like Digit, 106 ff.
    Number, 101 ff.
    Power, 102 ff.
    Products, 104
    Word, 94, 101
Pat and Mike Problem, 48
Pentagram, 128
Pentalpha, 128
Perfect Numbers, 41, 129
Pi or π, 50 ff., 54
Place Value, 16, 24
Planets, 133
Planudes, 150
Pleiades, 134
Pliny, 123
Position, Concept of, 16, 24
Postman Problem, 48
Powers, 77 ff., 102 ff.
Prime Curios, 45 ff.
    Numbers, 41 ff.
    Problems, 46 ff.
    Squares, 99
Proverbs, 116, 117, 126, 127, 138, 139, 141
Pythagoras, 50, 112, 151
Pythagorean Squares, 82

Quarantine, 148
Quinary System, 14

Radix, 13
Ramsay, Allan, 125
Real Numbers, 38 ff.
Rearrangements, 78 ff.
Recorde, Robert, 35

Reversals, 57, 80
Reversible Squares, 99 ff.
Rolling Log Problem, 83
Roman Numerals, 16 ff.

Sabbath, 135
Sabines, 139
Sailors' Spree Problem, 165
Saint Ives, 137
    Nicholas, 121
    Patrick, 122
School Tie Problem, 161
Score, 9, 12, 13, 14
Seamrog, 123
Seven, 2, 30, 113, 131 ff., 141
    Ages of Man, 133
    Bats, 133
    Champions, 136
    Colors, 133
    Deadly Sins, 136
    Gifts, 136
    Heavens, 137
    Hills, 131
    Sleepers, 136
    Stages of Drunkenness, 133
    Wise Men, 131
    Wonders, 131
Seventh Child, 132
Seventy, 149
Shakespeare, 20, 121, 124, 133, 145
Shamrock, 118, 123
Shanks, William, 51
Shepherd, Peruvian, 11
    Roman, 6
Shoemaker Problem, 159
Shoes Problem, 168
Shuldam's Square, 99
Sir Walter Raleigh's Ride, 166
Six, 29, 129 ff.
Smollett, Tobias, 125
Sodom, 143
Solomon, 51, 146
Solomon's Seal, 130
Span, 11, 139
Spectral Colors, 133

Spitting, 123
Square Curios, 88 ff.
  Roots, 84 ff.
Squared Battalion Problem, 175
Squares, 77 ff.
Stevin, 114
Stiffel, 152
Stock, 6, 9
Striking Clocks, 20
Subtractive Principle, 20
Superstition, 111 ff.
Surds, 49

Tabernacles, Feast of, 136
Tallies, 7 ff.
Tally Cutter, 8
  Stick, 8, 9
Ten, 12, 15 ff., 18, 141 ff.
Tennyson, 124
Ternary System, 4
Tertian Fever, 123
The 1-2-3-4-5 Problem, 34
Thirteen, 146 ff.
Thirteeners, 147
Thoth, 8
Thousand, 19, 81, 149
Three, 4, 27, 118 ff.
Three-legged Mare, 125
Thrice, 4, 119, 122
Tishri, 136, 142
Tithe, 143
Tom's Address Problem, 46
Tradition, 111 ff.
Trefoil, 122, 123
Triangle, 118
  Equilateral, 119
Tribunes, 142
Trillion, 150
Trinidad, 119
Trinity, 118, 122, 139
Twelfth Night, 145
Twelve, 15, 144 ff.
  Tables, 144
Twenty, 12, 15
Twice, 4, 120
Two, 27, 116 ff.

Two Fields Problem, 161
  Headed Eagle, 117

Unicorn, 115
Upper Ten, 142
Uranus, 134

Vantage Loaf, 147
Victoria, 154
Victory, The, 132
Vigesimal System, 14
Virgil, 113
Virgins, Parable of, 127, 143

Walrus, 1, 2
Walworth, 13
Ward, Artemus, 124
Wave Number, 155
Wellington, 154
Whilks, Cure for, 140
William the Conqueror, 153
Wine-bibbers Problem, 165
Wizard's Foot, 128, 129
Word Palindromes, 94, 101
  Squares, 94

Young Philatelists Problem, 176

Zero, 31
Zodiac, 145

Numbers of Interest not included in the General Index

Number	Page
25	79
28	41
37	64
48	81
76	79
81	84
99	152
101	45
102	104
111	104, 106
126	104
144	80
153	64, 65, 88, 104

169............. *80*
192............. *95*
219............. *95*
220............. *36*
273............. *95*
284............. *36*
327............. *95*
343............. *103*
370............. *88*
371............. *88*
407............. *88*
496............. *41*
595............. *105*
625............. *79*
666............. *21, 152*
688............. *104*
784............. *81*
1001............ *105*
1089............ *58, 65*
1331............ *103*
1680............ *81*

1729............ *89*
2025............ *84*
2592............ *81*
3025............ *84*
5776............ *79*
6336............ *105, 106*
6561............ *85*
8128............ *41*
8281............ *85*
9801............ *58, 65, 66, 84*
14641........... *102, 103*
69696.......... *102, 105*
88209.......... *66, 84*
141376......... *79*
142857......... *67*
275625......... *78*
285714......... *67*
390625......... *79*
494209......... *84*
998001......... *84*